MEXICAN ROAD RACE

Also by Patrick O'Connor

THE SOCIETY OF FOXES
FLIGHT OF THE PEACOCK
THE WATERMELON MYSTERY
THE BLACK TIGER
GUNPOWDER FOR WASHINGTON

Ives Washburn, Inc.
New York

MEXICAN ROAD RACE

by Patrick O'Connor

COPYRIGHT © 1957 BY IVES WASHBURN, INC.

All rights reserved, including the right to reproduce this book, or parts thereof, in any form, except for the inclusion of brief quotations in a review.

MANUFACTURED IN THE UNITED STATES OF AMERICA

DEDICATED

to my friend of long standing, Bill Dredge, engineering consultant and copilot on this race from border to border. Also to Bill Dredge's Morgan Plus Four.

MEXICAN ROAD RACE

1 WOODY HARTFORD squinted in the bright California sunlight which flooded the concrete bed of the Santa Barbara race track and then glanced at the stop watch in its socket on the dashboard of the Black Tiger.

The stop watch confirmed what he already knew. There were five more minutes to go in the race. Five minutes. That was time for two more laps, and to pass the two Ferraris ahead he had to make up half a lap on top of that. That meant he must drive two and a half laps in the time he could make only two circuits of the track with any degree of safety, even going full bore. All the Ferraris had to do was to hold their positions.

"Maybe I'll wind up on my head, but here goes," said Woody to himself. He pressed firmly on the accelerator pedal and the note of the Black Tiger's engine settled into a deep, sullen hum. He could feel his torso sink back into the seat as the car picked up speed. The concrete roadbed rushed toward him to slip beneath his wheels. He heard above the note of his engine a sea-like roar from the crowd and guessed that they were cheering him.

Woody had been racing the Black Tiger, a rear-engine sports car of revolutionary design, for a full year and had gained the title of "Last Lap Hartford." It always seemed that, whenever he won, he did so in the last lap of the thirty-minute race. Woody didn't plan it that way. It was his instinctive method of driving. He drove at his best when the odds were slimmest. Then he felt the challenge and was stimulated to rise to it.

There was a puff of smoke from the two Ferraris as they changed down to go into a bend. Woody knew the bend well. It was a right angle, broad, and on the surface nothing to worry about. But it had a slight cant in the wrong direction which made it difficult to control the skid or drift around it. He'd long ago learned that you don't steer a sports car around a bend. You set up a drift and control it until the car has skidded around, slipping sideways like a crab to a previously planned position. Then you step on the gas, pull out of the drift, and go on.

The two Ferraris had established their drift now. Like a couple of partners in a dance they slipped easily across the concrete, tires screaming, engines roaring, but in perfect control. Dave Kingston was driving the first and Kurt Kreuger the second. Both were old friends and rivals of Woody.

Woody put his right hand on the stubby gearshift of the Black Tiger to change down for the corner. He meant to change because he knew he needed the additional power to get around. It was the safe and sensible thing to do and every instinct told him to do it. But he didn't. He put his foot on the brake pedal and pressed hard twice, then glanced at the speedometer. It showed seventy-five miles an hour. Too fast for that corner. He hit the brake again, flicked the Black Tiger's wheel over, said, "Take it, baby," and hit the accelerator.

It seemed to Woody in the next few seconds that he was not driving a car over which he had control, but was a passenger in a balloon that moved where it wished. His wheels seemed to have lost all grip of the concrete roadbed. The chassis of the Black Tiger swung over in a big dip and stayed there. He caught a glimpse of Kingston's Ferrari right before his front wheels, and a pile of hay bales loomed suddenly in front of him. There was a high, protesting squeal from his tires, and above this and the noise of his engine a louder shout from the crowd behind the snow fence. Everything, for a while, seemed to be in slow motion. Woody caught a glimpse of the crowd breaking from the snow fence and scattering like dust before a puff of wind.

He was sure he was going to crack up but he had no sense of panic. He felt a heavy bump on the rear of the Black Tiger and realized that he had hit the hay bales. He stamped on the accelerator, heard the squeal of his rear tires, released the pedal, and stamped again. And suddenly the Black Tiger was back under control and around the corner headed down the straight. There was only one Ferrari ahead, Kurt Kreuger's.

"Baby," said Woody, "I don't know how you did it but you did it. Thanks."

Now a reaction set in. A flush of anxiety and relief went through his body and he realized he had taken a risk he had no right to in not changing down. He'd asked more of the Black Tiger than the Black Tiger was designed to give. He'd come through, but it was the result of some unexpected regaining of traction for which he could take no credit. He looked at Kreuger's Ferrari two hundred yards ahead, and, putting other thoughts from his mind, concentrated on the problem of passing Kurt. The stop watch said four minutes. Four minutes meant a lap and a half, or about fifteen bends with never so much as half a mile of straightaway. The Black Tiger could take a Ferrari on the straight, even a Ferrari driven by Kurt Kreuger whom Woody had never yet beaten. But the Black Tiger, because of her rear engine, couldn't corner like a Ferrari. She had the built-in cornering troubles of many rear-engined automobiles—unequal weight distribution throughout the chassis which made her temperamental on a corner.

But if Woody was to pass Kurt it would have to be on a corner, and Kurt was a wizard on corners.

Woody knew Kurt's driving characteristic well. He had what was almost a formula for shooting bends. He entered them wide and cut right in across the sharp angle of the bend to flatten it out, in effect halving the angle. The method was not especially Kurt's, but Kurt had brought it down to an exact science. He took the same path through each corner, lap after lap.

Woody stepped on the accelerator and overhauled the Ferrari on the third of a mile of straightaway which lay ahead. At the end of the straightaway was a series of S-bends. Kurt shot these in full bore and Woody did the same. Now came another straightaway, about a quarter of a mile, and then a switchback, a corner not quite so tight as a hairpin but one to be treated with the greatest respect.

Woody waited for Kurt to change down. He saw the puff of smoke from the Ferrari's exhaust and heard the roar of the engine. Then another puff and another roar. Kurt was going to take the jackknife in third. It was time for Woody to change now. He touched the brake and watched the tach needle move over to five thousand rpm. Then he declutched, hit the accelerator, and moved the gearshift into third, touched the accelerator once more and the clutch, and dropped down into second. He was in the corner. The Black Tiger drifted a little but the Ferrari clung to the inside like a leech.

Woody caught a glimpse of Kurt's left shoulder poised over the Ferrari's steering wheel. Woody's front wheels were almost level with the Ferrari's rear wheels. He knew what would happen now. Kurt would drift wide for a fraction of a second and Woody would be forced to drift wider, too, unless he again demanded more of the Black Tiger on a corner than he had a right to expect.

Woody was never conscious of making the decision. As the Ferrari left the inside of the corner in a nicely controlled drift, Woody pulled the Black Tiger over to get into the vacant place. For a moment he thought he was going to make it and had a second of exhilaration. Then he had a feeling that his steering rods had broken. The wheel twisted violently in his hands, the landscape spun around through a half circle, then a complete circle, and he knew he was spinning out, his car waltzing around on the track completely out of control.

Dave Kingston, whom he had already passed and

forgotten about, flashed by him within inches, a Jag clipped the front wheels of the Black Tiger and went careering off the track, and suddenly the Black Tiger was lying on its side in a cloud of dust and smoke.

All this seemed somehow unreal and remote to Woody. He sensed that he had had a bad crash but he could not thoroughly grasp the fact. He was still in the car, which was on its side, held in by his safety belt. His feet seemed very hot and he glanced down and saw a slow yellow tongue of flame creeping through the floor boards. Woody reached forward with his left hand and switched off the ignition. He kept saying "safety belt" to himself, and plucked ineffectually at it. But it was like a dream where serious danger presented itself and yet there was nothing to be done to avert it.

Then a man in white coveralls appeared with a carbon-dioxide extinguisher. Woody looked at him and said "Hello," and wondered why he should say anything so foolish in the circumstances.

More men appeared, and arms reached down and pulled him out of the driver's seat. A flood of sharp pain went through him when he was lifted up, and he heard the wailing of a siren. And then everything merged into blackness.

When Woody recovered consciousness he was in bed in a room which seemed to him quieter than any other place he had ever been in his life. He opened his eyes and saw a nurse sitting in a corner at a small table writing something. There was a scratchy sound caused either by the stiffness of her uniform or the movement of her pen. The nurse kept on writing, and Woody watched her with vague interest and thought over what had happened.

He was in a hospital. He had been in an accident. Then he remembered. The Black Tiger had cracked up. "Hey," he said, overwhelmed at the thought, "how's my car?"

The nurse turned quickly to him. "How do you feel?" she asked.

"Swell," said Woody, and tried to sit up. But he couldn't make it. He seemed to be tied down to the bed.

"You mustn't move," said the nurse, a woman in her fifties. "You've got two broken ribs and a broken collarbone. You're a very lucky young man to be alive at all."

"What about my car?" asked Woody, ignoring this report.

"I don't know anything about your car. There's a man downstairs waiting to see you. Doctor says you can see him for a few minutes if you promise not to get excited."

"What's his name?" asked Woody.

"Mr. McNess," replied the nurse.

"Good old Worm," said Woody, and added, "Gee, I hope he won't be mad."

William Orville Randolph McNess, proprietor of the McNess Union Service Station at Hermosa Beach, California, was Woody's boss, counselor, racing mate, and friend. A tall, thin Highland Scotsman, with an Aberdeen accent unchanged by fifteen years of residence in the United States, he was known as Worm because of his initials as well as for his elongated figure. Worm had two other noteworthy characteristics—a devotion to a mechanics textbook known as Davie's *Principles and Problems of Internal Combustion Engines,* which for him was the bible of automotive engineering, and a profound distrust of women. Worm was forty-five and an unalterable bachelor.

"Let him come on up," said Woody to the nurse. "I promise I'll lie quiet." She nodded and left.

Worm came in looking taller and more awkward than usual. A man who has spent most of his life bending over the engines of automobiles and working on his back under them, daily anointed with black grease, is quite out of place in an immaculate place such as a hospital ward. Worm acted as though one touch from him and everything would get soiled.

"Mon," he said in his clipped Highland Scots accent, "I saw ye spin out and turn over and I thought ye were dead."

"I took a chance on cutting in and didn't make it," said Woody. "She just went out of control. Did you tell Dad and Mom?"

"I phoned them and said you were in an accident but were all right. It cost a dollar and eighty-five cents." Woody laughed. Worm, he knew, couldn't help saying that. He believed himself a most generous man. "If the Hieland Scots have one fault at all," he would say, "it's that they're overliberal with money." Yet it really hurt Worm to part with hard cash.

"Thanks for calling, Worm," said Woody. "How's the Black Tiger?"

"Ah, don't trouble yer mind about her," said Worm.

"How is she?" Woody insisted.

"Weel," said Worm, "ye'll no' race her again. I can tell ye that. She's gutted oot by the fire. All that can be salvaged are a few parts." Woody closed his eyes in dismay.

"Gee," he said, "she was the finest car I ever drove. She was pedigree all the way through."

"Dinna carry on aboot it," said Worm gently. "Ye're alive and with only a few broken ribs. So be grateful for that. Don't worry about yere job, either. It'll be there for you when ye get oot and I'll keep ye on the pay roll."

"Thanks," said Woody, and he really meant it, not that he needed the money so much but because he knew what it meant for Worm to keep paying him when he wasn't working. Worm's profits from his service station were not large.

"Yer father and mother will be here tomorrow," said Worm. "I must get back to Hermosa Beach and look after the shop. But I'll come and see ye next weekend."

Woody didn't say anything. He was thinking that the Black Tiger wouldn't race again and it was he who had washed the car out. And he wondered whether the car was wrecked because of bad driving on his part. He tried to tell himself that it wasn't. But he'd taken unwarrantable risks on two corners. Then he remembered that a Jag had clipped him during the crash.

"What happened to the driver in the Jag that clipped me?" he asked.

"That was Pete Stephens," said Worm. "He's two rooms down from you wi' a broken arm."

"And the Jag?" Woody asked.

"They'll maybe be able tae salvage some parts," said Worm, looking at the floor.

Woody groaned. When Worm left he went over and over in his mind the question of whether he had been guilty of sheer, reckless driving, for which there was no more place on a race track than on a highway. Many drivers had been barred from racing because of recklessness.

Woody had a bad night of it and not altogether because of his broken bones.

2   WOODY stayed a week in the hospital at Santa Barbara. His torso was encased in an armor of elastic tape and one arm was strapped to his side to permit his collarbone to knit.

It was a miserable week, one filled with anxieties and worries. To begin with, his father and mother called on him and were obviously very concerned about the accident. Woody tried to convince them that any racing driver was likely to get into an accident at one time or another. But with safety helmets and safety belts the danger was not nearly so great as people unacquainted with racing thought. But his explanation sounded hollow even to himself.

Mr. Hartford took advantage of an interval when Woody's mother had left the ward to put a basic question to his son. "Woody," he said, "since you started earning your own living I've never tried to prevent you from doing anything you wanted to, though I've given you what advice I could.

"I'm not going to try to prevent you from continuing to race if you want to. But in fairness to yourself and I suppose to us, I have to ask you to consider seriously whether you should race again.

"You're lucky that you came through that crash

alive. Nobody doubts your courage. That is beside the point. But luck can run out, son. It has run out for many drivers before you. Let's face the facts. You can get killed. And a man's days on earth are short enough without his taking unneeded risks."

"Dad," said Woody, "a feller can get killed by just stepping off the sidewalk and being hit by a car."

"That's true," said Mr. Hartford. "But there's a question of care involved. People normally look before they step into the street. Have you seen the paper this morning?"

Woody shook his head.

"Well, there's a paragraph or two here that bear on what I'm driving at," said Mr. Hartford, and he handed Woody the paper. It was open at the sports page and the penciled paragraphs were in the weekly column of Mort Edghill, a prominent road-racing columnist. They read:

The accident to that up-and-coming race driver, Woody Hartford, at Santa Barbara, Saturday, raises a question often thought of but not discussed very openly among road-racing fraternities.

That question is—how much risk can a driver take to win a race? Or putting it another way, is a driver ever justified in risking his own life and that of other drivers by asking his car to perform feats which it is not built to perform?

This is not for a moment intended to cast any blame on young Hartford, who is reckoned one of the most talented drivers in the game today. Nobody knows precisely what happens at the moment a racing car goes out of control, but it looked to more than one experienced observer as if Hartford had no control of his car on a previous corner. That may not have been his fault. Hartford himself is the only man who can answer the question of whether he deliberately let his car out of control on a gambler's chance that he could regain control. Needless to say, a driver who does such a thing is asking others to share his risk and has no right to do so.

The columnist went on to repeat that he was not criticizing Woody and to pay tribute to his previous racing record. But it was plain that although there might be no official censure, the criticism was there nonetheless.

"That's a rotten thing to write," said Woody in anger, when he had read the column. "Those guys sit safely behind their typewriters and criticize the fellow behind the wheel who is risking his neck. I ought to go down there and punch him in the nose."

"Woody," said Mr. Hartford slowly and seriously, "you don't have to worry about this columnist. What you have to do is to ask yourself a question or two and answer them honestly. The first one you have to ask is, did you deliberately risk losing control, or did you believe you had a chance of retaining control; a reasonable chance?

"In other words, were you driving? Or were you trusting to fool's luck? And if you were trusting to fool's luck, is that a part of your nature? Is it so much a part of your nature that you would do it again and again, jeopardizing your own life and that of others until finally you kill yourself?

"I hate to have to put this to you, son, but I'm your

father and I have to do things like that. It takes a man, a real man, to ask himself that kind of questions and a real man to answer them.

"Whatever your answer is, Woody, I know it will be an honest one. And I'll never question it and never bring up the matter again."

Woody's next visitor was Mary Jane. Mary Jane was Woody's fiancée. He knew her attitude toward racing. There had been a time when Woody had been afraid to drive the Black Tiger and Mary Jane had been the one who had shown him that he mustn't give way to that fear. That had been a long time ago. But once he'd driven the car in a race and got over his fear, Mary Jane had wanted him to give up racing.

She still wanted him to, and assumed that he was willing to do so now. "In a way I'm glad you had the accident," she said. "Now you can see that you don't have to keep racing until you kill yourself. Besides, we've got to save up some money if we're ever going to be married."

Woody said nothing. He himself didn't know whether he would ever race again. He wanted to talk to Worm and Kurt Kreuger and Dave Kingston. They were racing drivers and they understood about racing. They would have read the column by Mort Edghill. He wanted to know their opinion of whether he had a suicidal streak of recklessness in him which would make him an unpredictably dangerous driver.

The third day of his stay in the hospital Kurt came to see Woody. He was on his way up to San Francisco, he explained, to take possession of a new Ferrari which had just arrived. He was a stubby, heavy-set man with a very slow manner of talking. He seemed to take great care in anything he did and did nothing in a hurry.

Despite his worries, Woody smiled at the precise way in which Kurt put a chair by his bed and then sat down in it as if he didn't quite trust it to hold his hundred and sixty-five pounds.

"Gee, I'm sure glad you called, Kurt," Woody said. "I've been wanting to see you and Dave Kingston."

Kurt's pale blue eyes looked straight at Woody with great interest. "How are you feeling?" he asked slowly.

"Physically swell," replied Woody. "But I've been worried. Did you see that piece in the paper by Mort Edghill?"

Kurt nodded.

"That's what I'm worried about," said Woody. "I'm worried about the time I passed Dave and the accident when I tried to pass you. I'm worried about whether I took a foolhardy chance that I had no right to take, and I'm worried about whether I'm likely to keep on taking chances like that. You've seen me drive. I wish you'd tell me."

Kurt, as slow and deliberate as a tortoise, took a packet of cigarettes out of his pocket, selected one, read the brand on the cigarette paper although he knew it very well, and then put the cigarette in his mouth.

"There was a meeting of some of the drivers right after the race in one of the hotel rooms," he said slowly. "I came up here to see you but you were still blacked out so I went back to the hotel and there was this meeting." He searched around in his pockets for a match, chose one from the box and lit his cigarette.

"What was the meeting about?" asked Woody impatiently.

"About you going on your head," said Kurt.

"What did the fellows think?" asked Woody.

"Well, I'm not mentioning any names," said Kurt, "but some of them blamed the Black Tiger and said it always was a cranky car, and it had killed Randy." Woody nodded. In the early days of the Black Tiger's history, brake failure had killed the driver, Captain Randolph, and the car had got the reputation of a killer.

"Some of them said that you were a harebrained kid and should be ruled off the track," Kurt continued. He saw the color drain from Woody's face.

"I didn't agree with them," Kurt said. "I don't think you're a harebrained kid. I think you're a pretty smart driver. You aren't any crazier than any other sportscar driver and some of them are the sanest people on earth. One day you'll make a real swell driver. If you live that long."

"I'm not looking to get myself killed," said Woody.

Kurt continued slowly and methodically, as if he hadn't heard him, "You've got only one fault," he said, "and you can't be blamed for it. You're young. People who aren't young any longer forget what it's like to be that way. They forget that part of being young is taking fool chances. You stop being young round about the time you start figuring the odds on any particular chance coming off. That's the difference between being a kid and being an adult. A green kid will take any kind of a chance because he's sure he'll come through. A grown man figures the odds first. Then, if he has to take a chance, he takes it. But he knows what he's in for if the chance is against him. It takes guts, not just foolhardiness, to be a full-grown man."

Kurt took the cigarette from his mouth and crushed it out in an ash tray. "I smoke too much," he said. "Sometimes I think I talk too much, too."

"I'm sure grateful that you came and talked to me," said Woody. "I think I understand what you mean."

"Did you figure the Black Tiger could hold the road when you cut in on that corner?" Kurt asked.

Woody thought for a long time. "I don't know whether I can answer that," he said. "I just cut over and took a chance on it. That's as honest as I can be about it."

"What about the time you passed Dave Kingston in high on the right-angle bend?"

"Same thing," said Woody. "I knew I should change down. But something made me take a chance on barreling through in high. I went to change down but I didn't. I didn't have control around the corner."

Kurt laughed, a deep rumble of pleasure. "Dave said you looked like a cow on ice skates. He swallowed a nickel's worth of chewing gum and has had indigestion ever since. Look, Woody," he continued, "what happened to you happens to everybody who ever took a car round a race track. Happens to drivers on the highway all the time, too. They get the idea they can cut in or take a corner blind. And sometimes it comes off and sometimes they wind up in the morgue.

"All you've got to do is grow up. You've got to learn to drive a car all the time and never let the car drive you. You've got to learn when to control an impulse as foolheaded and when to act on it because the impulse comes from experience and not recklessness. There isn't any formula for that. It just takes experience."

Kurt got up slowly from his chair and carefully put it back against the wall. "About that drivers' meeting," he said, "there's to be a meeting of the Southern California Sports Car Association officials to inquire into the accident. It's strictly a track officials' meeting but they may call on some of the drivers. Don't take it too hard. They have to have these inquiries. They have to decide whether there's any negligence leading to an accident."

"You mean they might suspend me?" asked Woody.

"Not if Dave and I can help it," said Kurt slowly. "Of course our opinion may not be asked. But we'll see what happens. It won't be for a couple of weeks."

3 THE MEETING of the Southern California Sports Car Association to inquire into Woody's accident was held in a small banquet room of a downtown hotel in Los Angeles. By that time Woody was out of the hospital and although his arm was still immobilized to allow his collarbone to set, he was able to return to the service station in Hermosa Beach to help Worm. His work was limited to filling gas tanks and general servicing of cars. He could do none of the mechanical repair work for which Worm's service station was noted and this was piling up.

Woody received notice of the meeting well in advance and Worm said he'd drive him to town. Woody was very worried. He was afraid he would be suspended from driving in SCSCA events and that might well mean suspension from driving in events sponsored by other clubs.

Worm did his best to cheer him up. "Dinna worry, laddie," he said. "They must hold a meeting. Every accident has to be investigated by the club. But you've nothing to fear." But he didn't say this with any great conviction. Privately he was afraid Woody would be suspended.

There was another matter to worry Woody at this

time also. The Black Tiger was not his car. It belonged to Rocky Randolph, the nineteen-year-old daughter of Captain Jim Randolph, who had been killed in an earlier crash in the Black Tiger. After that accident, nobody had wanted to drive the Black Tiger. Rocky had asked Woody to drive it, explaining that if the car got a bad name all her father's investments in the factory in Italy which made Black Tiger would be jeopardized.

Woody had driven the car although he was afraid of it, and had done well. But now it was wrecked, and he wondered how Rocky would take the news. She was in Italy, visiting the factory with her aunt Babs, but was due back soon.

There was plenty on his mind when he entered the small banquet room of the Chase Hotel in Los Angeles to wait for the hearing to start. There were only a dozen officials of the club—the president, Jim Withers, secretary, Tom Western, and three or four of the flagmen who had been on duty at the race. They nodded to Woody and spoke in a friendly way to him before the proceedings started.

"You're not on trial for anything here," Jim Withers said. "This isn't a court, so don't look so worried. It's just an inquiry into the accident to see whether such accidents can be prevented in future. As you know, we don't race cars to hurt or kill ourselves. We do it to improve automobile performance, safety, and driving skill."

Withers repeated these remarks when he called the meeting to order. Then he asked the flagman nearest the accident site about the condition of the roadbed.

Had there been any oil on it? Was there any unusual quantity of loose gravel about? Was he sure that the cutoff markers, warning drivers to slow down for the corner, had been in place?

This line of questioning confirmed what everybody knew. There was nothing about the track itself which could be blamed for the crash.

Withers next went into the mechanical condition of the Black Tiger. He asked whether any of the pit crew were present, and Worm stood up. It was established that the Black Tiger had passed its technical inspection before the race, and had passed the final inspection in the line-up. The tires were in good shape immediately before the start of the race, and there was no reason to doubt the efficiency of the brakes.

Then Withers turned to Woody. "The Black Tiger has a heavy accident record," he said. "The former driver, Captain Randolph, was first seriously hurt and then killed in the car, and in each case through a mechanical failure. It's a new car and probably there are still a few bugs in it. We must bear that in mind."

Woody sensed that Withers was giving him an opportunity to blame the car for the accident by saying that either the steering, brakes, or clutch had failed. Burned out by the fire, there would be no way of checking his statement. But Woody loved the Black Tiger. The car had had a bad name once before and he was determined that that bad name would not be restored.

"No, sir," he said. "There was nothing the matter with the mechanical condition of the Black Tiger."

"One of the flagmen has told us," said Withers, "that

you looked as though you were out of control on a previous corner when you passed Dave Kingston. Are you sure your brakes weren't beginning to fade?"

"There wasn't anything the matter with the brakes," said Woody. "They held up throughout the race and gave me no trouble at all."

"Steering?" asked Withers.

"It was O.K.," said Woody. There was silence in the room except for his own voice, and that sounded oddly high to him.

"What, in your opinion, was the cause of the crash?" Withers asked quietly.

This was the question Woody had been dreading. He'd gone over it time and again in his own mind and the only real answer was that he'd taken a risk that didn't come off.

"The accident was my fault," he said, his voice low although still audible in the quiet room. "I don't know how to put it properly. I went in the turn over my head and spun out. I asked more of the car than I had a right to. It was bad judgment."

Everybody in the room was looking at Woody. Withers had a pencil in his hand and kept sliding it end over end through his fingers on the desk before him.

"Was that what happened on the previous corner when you looked out of control and hit the hay bales?" he asked.

"Yes," said Woody. "I didn't change down. I went through in high and lost too many rpms."

"There was no mechanical damage to your car after you hit the hay bales?"

"No. Nothing to affect its driving characteristics or control."

"I see." There was a silence. Nobody seemed to know what to say next. Woody felt that it was all up for him and he would certainly be suspended. That feeling was strengthened by Withers' next words.

"We've heard a few complaints, none of them official," he said, "about your driving methods from other drivers. Some seem to think that you are a trifle foolhardy and reckless and an unnecessary danger in a sport which contains enough risks of its own."

"Mr. President," said Kurt, who was sitting in the back of the room, "that's just what some of the drivers say. But there are others like myself who think Woody is a top driver although maybe a little inexperienced."

"Thank you, Kurt," said Withers. "I'm just mentioning this unofficially. Personal feelings are always involved in this kind of talk and unless specific instances are cited and a complaint made officially we can pay no real attention to this kind of criticism.

"I told you before that the object of this meeting was to ascertain the cause of the accident. Mr. Hartford has admitted that the cause of the accident was bad judgment on his part.

"Bad judgment itself is no crime. We have all been guilty of it. What we must decide here is whether this bad judgment is part of the nature of the driver, Mr. Hartford. Whether, in fact, he has a streak of recklessness and foolhardiness for which there is no place on a race track. If all but the members of this committee will leave the room, we will discuss the matter and let you know our decision."

There were a number of coughs and the noise of scraping chairs and Woody found himself in the corridor outside. Nobody said anything to him, not even Worm. They were all talking about other matters in a strained kind of way, but Woody could summon up no interest in their conversation. This was the crisis of his racing career. A driver once suspended has a hard time living down his suspension. When they were called back into the room, he was sure he would be ruled off the SCSCA tracks, at least for three or four events.

"We've talked this whole thing over," said Withers, "and I want you to know that our decision is unanimous.

"It is that Woody Hartford by his own admission was guilty of bad judgment and that resulted in the accident. However, we have found nothing in his previous record to indicate he is a chronically reckless driver, the kind that shouldn't be allowed on any race track or on any highway for that matter.

"So there is no question of his suspension. He remains a fully-qualified driver under the rules of the Association, and my colleagues join me in wishing him a speedy recovery from his injuries and many more years of racing ahead."

Woody felt so relieved he could only grin and make ineffectual noises in reply to the congratulations of the friends who swarmed around him.

With the removal of the one cloud which had hung over his career, his other troubles seemed very small and easy to manage. On the following day the sports pages of the Los Angeles papers carried stories saying he had not been suspended and praising him for his frank admission that the accident had been the result of bad judgment.

A paragraph in Mort Edghill's column particularly pleased him. It read:

It takes guts to win a road race, and it takes guts to admit that your own bad judgment was the cause of an accident.

Woody Hartford has shown he has both these kinds of courage. He could have hid behind some pretended mechanical defect in his car but he didn't. We believe that he'll go on to become one of the truly great drivers of the United States.

But Mary Jane took another point of view. "You've shown that you are a good driver and you've had your accident," she said. "Now it's time to stop thinking about sports-car racing and settle down to serious things like saving money for a down payment on a house. You'll never get a down payment together if you spend every penny you make on sports cars."

"Oh, we'll get the money for the down payment someday," said Woody.

"Woody Hartford," Mary Jane said, "I hope you're not thinking of racing again."

"Not much sense thinking about it," said Woody. "The Black Tiger's wrecked and there isn't a car for me to drive."

Mary Jane could not feel much satisfaction with this answer.

4 WOODY'S ACCIDENT had occurred in August, and it was now mid-September—a most important time of the year for Worm, for September was the month when he gave an annual overhaul to his venerable 1928 Dodge, which was the apple of Worm's eye and which he permitted no one to drive but himself.

Woody sometimes thought that, in Worm's opinion, the automobile had reached perfection in 1928 with the arrival on the market of that year's model Dodge. Worm, in his overhaul of the car which went all the way from ignition to transmission and the rear end, never added a single item of improved equipment. He stuck strictly to 1928 specifications and spent months getting together parts such as connecting-rod bearings and piston rings which were no longer manufactured.

The Dodge did have a self-starter, but Worm more often than not started it with a crank, first adjusting the ignition and throttle levers on the steering wheel with as much care as a jeweler weighing out gold.

When Worm was overhauling his Dodge he became philosophical and quick-tempered by turns. In his philosophical moments he expounded on the finer points of automobile engineering and the cars he had driven in his youth. During the quick-tempered periods, he denounced all automobiles as buckets of bolts, and said only men of unsound mind turned to garage work for a living.

He was in a philosophical frame of mind now. He had found some main bearings which could be adapted to the crankshaft of the Dodge and his mind was at ease for the moment. He hunched his shoulders forward, put two long, lean fingers in the breast pocket of his coveralls, and extracted a cigarette.

"How are ye feeling?" he asked Woody.

Woody, who had just finished changing the plugs on a Studebaker "Golden Hawk," straightened up, worked his shoulders, and said, "Swell. Just as good as new."

"Want a cup of coffee?" asked Worm. Woody was mildly surprised. Worm's service station boasted an automatic coffee machine, which squirted an evil-tasting brew into paper cups in return for a dime. Worm rarely squandered a dime in the machine.

"Thanks," said Woody, and Worm got the coffee for him.

"Ye'll be planning and scheming and longing to do some more racing and bust your ribs again, no doubt," said Worm.

"Isn't any sense to it," said Woody sadly. "No car. No dough. I couldn't even get enough together to enter the soapbox derby."

Worm paid no attention to this. It was his habit to ignore any mention of money. "What does yer lassie say about ye racing again?" he asked.

"She doesn't think I ever will."

"Will ye?"

"If I get a chance—yes."

Worm threw his cigarette on the floor and ground it to shreds as if it were a snake. He glanced at the clock and noted that it was ten minutes to five and time to get ready to close up the shop for the day.

"Ye may get yer chance before ye think," he said. "I had a letter this morning from Rocky."

"You did?" cried Woody. "Where is she? What did she say?"

"She was in New York and she's arriving back from Italy at the international airport by plane tonight. Seven o'clock."

"Cripes," said Woody. "I've got to meet her. I want to tell her myself about the Black Tiger. Gee, I hope she's not going to be too mad with me."

"She knows about the Black Tiger," said Worm. "I cabled her after the accident and I sent her a letter. The cable cost four dollars and eighty-eight cents."

"What did she say?" asked Woody.

"She didn't say anything about the wreck," replied Worm. "She said the factory has gone into production with a new model of the Black Tiger—the Black Tiger, Mark II."

"A new model?" cried Woody. "I wonder whether they've licked that weight-distribution problem? Cripes, I've got to find out all about this right now. Seven o'clock, you say? Why didn't you tell me before?"

"Because if I had told ye this morning," said Worm cannily, "ye'd not have been able to work all day. Ye're not a man who can take news and not let it interfere with his work."

Woody snorted, threw the paper cup from which he

had been drinking his coffee into a waste bucket, put his hand in his pocket and came up with a handful of change. He walked over to the wall telephone, took the receiver off the hook, and then paused. Worm watched him with just a trace of a smile on his thin lips.

Woody was in a delicate position. He had promised to take Mary Jane to a movie that night. But the promise had been made before he knew that Rocky was arriving back from Italy with news of a new model of the Black Tiger. Now he wanted to meet Rocky and find out about the car and tell her himself of the accident. And Mary Jane, although she didn't dislike Rocky, wasn't very friendly toward her. Furthermore, Mary Jane was dead set against Woody's doing any more sports-car racing. In short, Mary Jane would be good and mad if he canceled the movie date to meet Rocky.

"Heck," said Woody to himself, "dames are just not cut out to understand men. They don't think the same way." He braced himself, inserted the dime, and dialed Mary Jane's number. She answered the phone immediately.

"Hi," said Woody, trying a new tactic. "I got some good news for you."

Mary Jane's voice sounded dubious. "You have?" she asked.

"Yep," said Woody, plunging on recklessly. "Wait until you hear this. They're putting out a new model of the Black Tiger. A Mark II. It's in production right now in Italy."

"Oh," said Mary Jane, and her voice was as distant as if she were speaking from the bottom of a well.

"That's right," said Woody. "Isn't that swell? And Rocky's arriving by plane tonight so I thought—"

"You thought you'd like to break our date and go and meet her," Mary Jane cut in crisply.

"No, honey," said Woody, "I don't want to break our date. I thought maybe you'd like to come out to the airport with me and meet her and we could all spend the evening together." When he had said this, Woody realized immediately it was the worst possible thing he could say. He got no comfort from seeing Worm's shoulders shaking slightly with subdued laughter.

"Woody Hartford," said Mary Jane, "if you want to go out to the airport to meet Rocky, you can go. But I'm not coming with you. I'm going to see *War and Peace* at the Criton." And she hung up.

Woody went to see *War and Peace,* too. He thought the title was apt to describe the state of affairs between him and Mary Jane, for it was not a pleasant evening. He didn't get much out of the movie, either. It was difficult to concentrate on Napoleon's retreat from Moscow when he kept thinking of the Black Tiger, Mark II, and Rocky arriving, and whether he would ever be able to race the new car.

The next day Worm told him that he'd met Rocky himself and gave Woody the address of her hotel in Los Angeles. Rocky lived in San Diego but would be in Los Angeles for a couple of days. Woody called her but she was out all morning. In the end Worm told him to take the rest of the day off and go to see Rocky. He knew his young assistant wouldn't be of much help around the garage until he'd found out about the new car.

Woody had hardly left the garage before Mary Jane called and asked for him.

"He's gone into Los Angeles," said Worm cautiously.

"Oh. I suppose he's gone to see Rocky," said Mary Jane.

"No," he said. "He's going tae see her all right. But what he most wants is to hear about the new Black Tiger. In a manner of speaking, he's gone to see a car, not a girl." He hoped that Mary Jane would understand this. Mary Jane thanked him and hung up.

Rocky was out shopping when Woody arrived at her hotel, and he had to wait for an hour and a half before she returned. When they met, she was loaded down with parcels and accompanied by her aunt, a middle-aged, gray-haired, tall, handsome woman, who was introduced to him as Babs.

"I expect you two will want to talk together," said Babs. "Here, give me the parcels and I'll take them upstairs."

Rocky turned to Woody. She looked even prettier than he remembered and more grown up. "Goodness," she said with genuine concern, "you look thin. Are you all over the accident?"

"Sure," said Woody. "Let's go into the fountain and get a Coke. How are you? Did you have a good time?" He reeled off a list of questions that Rocky did her best to cope with.

Finally, with their Cokes before them, he got down to the real question. "Tell me about the new Black Tiger," he said. "What's she like? Is there much change?"

"She's the mostest," said Rocky. "You've never even

thought of a car like the Mark II. She has a six-cylinder rear-opposed engine. The engine has been moved forward almost ten inches to take care of weight distribution, and the engine block is made of a new titanium alloy developed in Italy. It's stronger than the best aluminum block and lighter and about equal in conducting heat."

Woody had heard vaguely of titanium, a new element identified some time before World War II. He knew it was used in high-speed jet-plane engines because it was so tough and light.

"What's the engine capacity?" he asked.

"Three and a half liters," said Rocky. "That's just double the displacement of our old MG. The factory clocked a stock model on the straight at a hundred and seventy-five miles an hour. That's without any modifications and using gasoline. But wait until you hear the rest. This car's full of new stuff.

"There's a new steel alloy in the pistons and valves, crankshaft, and connecting rods. It's harder than chrome steel. The cylinders are sleeves. When they show wear all you have to do is replace them. No rebores.

"And there's more than that. The car uses a fuel injection system. No carburetor. Raw gas is squirted directly into the cylinders with the air intake coming through the intake valve as usual."

"What about weight and horsepower?" Woody asked.

"Hold on to your hat," said Rocky. "The weight in racing trim—that is with a twenty-gallon tank full of gas—is just over fourteen hundred pounds. And the

Mark II develops three hundred and forty horsepower at peak rpm."

"Brother," said Woody reverently. "The Black Tiger, Mark II, weighs less than an MG but its peak horsepower is well ahead of a D-Model Jaguar. This one is a real bomb."

"There's one more item," concluded Rocky, "with the new titanium alloy block, the car is equipped with a sealed-in cooling system. The old Black Tiger was air-cooled. But the designers believe the sealed-in cooling system will be even more efficient."

Woody's head was swirling with specifications. A hundred and seventy-five miles an hour on the straight! Three hundred and forty horses at peak revs! Fuel injection! Sealed and pressurized cooling system! It was more than he had dreamed of in any one car.

"Do you have printed dope?" he asked.

"Lots," said Rocky. "Photos and drawings. But you don't have to wade through them. The first model is going to arrive in San Francisco on the *Conti da Roma* next Thursday. It's consigned to me. If you like, you can come up with me and get it. Maybe Worm would come, too. I want to drive her back down, but we'll have to check it over and see if everything's O.K. I'd like Worm to check it."

"Worm would give his right arm to do it," said Woody enthusiastically. And he knew this was true. For although Worm in his bad moments denounced all automobiles as buckets of bolts, he had a deep love for them and especially for sports cars.

5

"MARY JANE," said her mother, Mrs. Simmons, "sit down a minute. I want to talk to you." Mary Jane sat down obediently but with some dismay for she knew what the topic of conversation was going to be.

Mrs. Simmons' first words confirmed this suspicion. "I'm worried about what's going on between you and Woody," she said. "He's hardly called you in two weeks. Just what is the matter?"

"Oh, you wouldn't understand," said Mary Jane.

Mrs. Simmons sighed. She wondered just why it was that daughters always seemed to believe their mothers couldn't understand their problems.

"Well, I certainly won't understand unless I'm told what the trouble is," she said. "Why don't you tell me and then we'll see whether I can understand or not. There's no loss in that."

Mary Jane didn't want to hurt her mother. And she needed someone to talk to. So she gave in.

"Woody thinks more about sports cars than he does about me," she said almost fiercely. "That's it in a nutshell. Gosh, if I want to look for him, all I've got to do is move some car and there he is, flat on his back, with his silly face all covered with grease. We've been engaged for six months now and he hasn't saved a single penny to buy furniture with or for a house. I'm just some kind of a convenience he calls up when there isn't a car for him to drive or repair."

"But cars are Woody's job, dear," said Mrs. Simmons gently. "I expect that with this new car he's just very excited about it and it will wear off."

"I said you wouldn't understand," said Mary Jane unfairly. "It isn't just the new car. It's his whole attitude. His entire life centers around cars. He hasn't any other kind of thought in his head. And if it wasn't this new Black Tiger that I'm sick to death of hearing about it would be some other car. What kind of married life will I have with him always ready to drop everything to go off and see some stupid old car?"

Mrs. Simmons wanted to say that most men spent a great part of their time even after working hours thinking about their jobs, and her own father brought work home from the office almost every night of the week. But she decided to say nothing for the time being.

"Then there's that Rocky girl," said Mary Jane. "She spends more time with Woody than I do. She pretends that she's just keen on cars and racing and building up sales for this Black Tiger on the West Coast. But I'll bet all she's after is a husband."

"Rocky?" said Mrs. Simmons innocently. "Who's Rocky?"

"Oh, Mother, I've told you a thousand times," said Mary Jane. "Rocky's the daughter of Captain Jim Randolph who got killed driving the Black Tiger. All his money was tied up in the factory which made the Black

Tiger and is making this new car. Rocky now owns all her father's shares in the factory, and she's opening an agency to take orders for the cars here, with Woody and Worm helping or sharing in it somehow. And I just know that she's after Woody's scalp. And he's so dumb he'll let her take it and it will serve him right." At that point Mary Jane started to cry.

Mrs. Simmons didn't know what to say to that. The situation was far more serious than she had thought. She put her arms around her daughter's shoulders to comfort her, and decided she had better talk the whole situation over with her husband. Not that he would be of much help, she reflected. He was all wrapped up in his insurance business, but he should certainly be told how unhappy his daughter was.

Two weeks before this, Woody, Rocky, and Worm had gone up to San Francisco to take possession of the new Black Tiger, Mark II. Worm had checked it over after it was uncrated in a San Francisco garage and had been cleaned of the special coating sprayed over it to preserve it during the sea voyage.

With the car had come a complete set of blueprints and a mechanic's manual as thick as a volume of an encyclopedia. This showed three views of every part on the car and was actually a catalogue as well as an instruction manual. It was printed in English, and with its aid Worm had no difficulty in checking lubrication, grease, ignition and other vital items.

The Black Tiger, Mark II, proved even more beautiful to Woody than the photos Rocky had shown him. It was a two-seater roadster, with separate red-leather bucket seats, safety belts, padded dashboard, solid magnesium knock-off wheels, and all the instruments, including speedometer, tachometer, oil and coolant temperature gauges, and finally a big clock with a sweep second hand that could be reset like a stop watch. In racing without a co-driver, a metal cockpit cover fitted over the passenger's side to cut down air turbulence. It was, as Rocky had said of it, "the mostest." Woody and Rocky drove it back from San Francisco to Los Angeles after clearing up the paper work, never taking it over sixty-five miles an hour in high so as to break the engine in gently.

But even confined to sixty-five miles an hour during the break-in trip, Woody was delighted at the handling qualities of the car. He longed to get it on a track and check acceleration through the gears and crank it through some tight corners. He had by now given Rocky the full details of the accident to the Mark I, as the first Black Tiger was called, and also told her of the Southern California Sports Car Association inquiry into the accident.

Rocky said it was nothing that could be helped and it was silly to talk of Woody having used bad judgment.

"How do you know what a car will do until you try it?" she said in her practical way. "I'm sure Dad would have done the same thing. You've got to take a risk once in a while."

"Well," said Woody, "there was some talk among some of the drivers—not Kurt or Worm or Dave Kingston, but some of the others—that I was foolhardy. I wish the sports writers hadn't hung that 'Last-lap Hartford' tag on me. It kind of supports the talk that in the last couple of laps I throw all caution to the winds and just go full bore."

"Well, don't you?" asked Rocky.

"No," said Woody. "Not exactly. I don't see any sense getting washed out in the first fifteen or twenty laps. I figure that's the time to study the other drivers, find out something about the corners, and how the car's behaving. Then pour on the coal right at the end."

Rocky laughed. "We'll see what you can do with this little bomb," she said.

"Gosh," said Woody, "you mean you're going to let me drive it in competition?"

"Certainly," replied Rocky. "I'm going to drive it in the ladies' races and you're going to drive it in the other events. But this isn't purely sport any longer. This is the only Black Tiger, Mark II, in the country—and probably will be the only one until somebody puts in an order.

"This little buggy costs six thousand five hundred dollars landed in San Francisco. That's a lot of money. The car has got to make a name for itself before people start putting in orders. And it's up to us to make that name. Otherwise, the day will come when little Rocky isn't going to eat. All my money, as you know, is tied up in the Black Tiger factory."

"Don't worry," said Woody jubilantly. "We'll hang up a line of firsts that will have everybody ordering Black Tigers like they all went crazy for Jags and then Mercedes Benz Superlights. Boy, this little bomb should be able to take on all comers."

"When we've got the bugs worked out of it," cautioned Rocky soberly. "There will have to be some trial runs before we enter any races."

A great many things happened one after the other when Rocky took possession of the first Mark II. She and Woody and Worm and her Aunt Babs had a number of conferences in which Worm pointed out that if a sales agency for the Black Tiger was to be opened, it would be best to locate it in or near Los Angeles, which had the greatest number of sports-car fans of any city in the nation.

Rocky decided that the Black Tiger agency should be opened in Hermosa Beach close to Los Angeles on an empty lot opposite Worm's garage. The lot had a small office that had belonged to a real-estate broker and could be rented on a monthly basis for a small sum. Soon there was a sign over the office saying "BLACK TIGER MOTORS," and the Mark II was on display.

The car attracted a lot of attention. Rocky handled all the inquiries. But the price of sixty-five hundred dollars, the difficulty of financing an untested foreign car through a bank, and the fact that orders had to be placed with the factory in Italy, with a minimum of two months before delivery, cooled off prospective customers.

It was plain, as Rocky had foreseen, that there would be no serious interest until the Mark II had made a name for itself in competition. A week after the car arrived, Woody and Rocky took the Mark II out to a dry lake near Lancaster. Here there was a four-mile circle of hard, salt-caked sand—a perfect surface for speed trials, flat and without cracks or soggy areas.

Woody tried the Mark II out from a standing start and was astounded at the acceleration. Each gear change seemed to equip the car with an extra jet engine, so that it thrust forward like a greyhound after each change, the tachometer needle sweeping over the dial. He wound the Mark II up tight in high and watched the speedometer needle climb to one hundred and sixty-five before he had to slow down to avoid heading off into the bush. He still had plenty of torque and was satisfied that it could make the boasted hundred and seventy-five and maybe more.

The problem that really interested him was cornering. The old Mark I had been tender on corners because of the weight it carried over the rear wheels with little to compensate it over the front wheels.

He put some flags in the bed of the salt lake to simulate a couple of hairpins and a right-angle bend. "I'll try them easy first," he said, "just to get the feel of it. Then I'll see how she reacts when I set up a drift and pour the power to her."

He tried the right-angle bend first, entering it wide and cutting in toward the inside to straighten out the corner in the approved style. The first couple of tries he muffed it, braking and then going into his drift too soon, so that he came out wide.

Rocky looked puzzled. "Anything the matter?" she asked after the second attempt.

"No," said Woody. "I just can't get it into my thick skull how tight she sticks. I keep shutting off too soon, whereas actually I can keep going much longer. It's a funny feeling. You kinda have to learn to drive again."

He tried several more times on the right angle. The first time he muffed it again, but on the second try he set up the power drift when he was almost tight against the inside of the corner. The result was astonishing. When he straightened out and changed up, he was still on the inside of the corner instead of out in the middle or somewhat over to the far side as had usually been the case with the Mark I.

"Man," he said to Rocky, "nobody would believe this if I told them. They'll have to see it."

He tried the hairpins next, and had the same trouble—shutting off too soon. But when he finally got the knack of it, he went around the hairpins as if fixed to a rail on the inside of the bend.

"Rocky," he said jubilantly, "there's nothing in the world I know of can beat this Mark II. Nothing. Get in and try. Remember, don't shut off too soon. When you think it's time to shut off hold it for a few seconds and then brake and change down."

Rocky spent the next half hour trying the right angle and the hairpins herself. She returned as jubilant as Woody.

"What about the Pomona race meeting?" asked Woody. "It's in three weeks. Do you suppose we could enter?"

"Pomona it is," said Rocky, holding out a slim hand in her driving glove. Woody was sure he would never feel happier in all his life.

6 WORM SQUINTED over the tool kit which he had carefully laid out in the Mark II's pit area at Pomona, giving everything a final check. A set of metric wrenches lay in a toolbox as neatly as soldiers on parade, each one in its place. There was a set of screw drivers, sockets, and end wrenches, four extra tires mounted on wheels and inflated to the correct pressure, two floor jacks, carbon-dioxide fire extinguisher . . . Everything was there and in place.

He turned to Rocky, looking pert in her racing helmet and white coveralls as she pulled on her driving gloves. "Come in if you've any trouble at all," he cautioned. "Remember yon car's new. There's no sense driving the guts out of her in her first race."

Rocky smiled and nodded. She had just come back from ten practice laps and was waiting the call to bring the Black Tiger, Mark II, down to the starting area for the Ladies' Race. She would be the first to drive the Mark II in competition in the United States and she was very proud of the honor.

"I don't think there'll be any trouble," she said. "She handles like a dream."

"What's the track like?" asked Woody.

He had not raced at Pomona before and neither had

Rocky. "Real sporty," she replied. "There're a couple of turns over on the far side that would put a curl in your hair. Narrow. No camber. Then you dive down under a bridge through a cutting and it's real spooky." She spoke with excitement and without a trace of nervousness and anxiety. Woody envied Rocky her pre-race attitude. She always seemed full of confidence. He, himself, never felt quite comfortable until he had a couple of laps under his belt.

"Your attention, please," said the announcer over the loud-speaker. "All cars for event number three—the Ladies' Race—get down to the starting area immediately."

"This is it," said Rocky, and climbed behind the wheel.

Woody got in beside her, and Worm said, "Good luck. I'll stay here." He held out a bony hand, and Rocky started off amid a school of cars for the starting area.

Her position was in the middle of the pack, tenth in a field of seventeen. There were two Jags ahead, two Ferraris, and a Cunningham that she could see. She adjusted the chin strap of her racing helmet, put her goggles in place, and Woody helped her fasten her safety belt. He took a last-minute look at the tires, and a race official came through the pack of cars checking off the entrants on a sheet held on a clip board. There were surges of acceleration around them as drivers sought to prevent plugs from fouling. Then these noises died down into an expectant silence.

Woody shook Rocky's hand. "Good luck," he said. There was nothing more to say, for Rocky was a completely competent driver and there was no advice he could offer. For a second he hesitated over whether to remind her not to shut off too soon. But he, himself, disliked last-minute advice before races, so he said nothing but left the starting area and went behind the safety line. Worm was there, having left the racing pit to witness the start.

The starter went down through the pack of cars, checking to see that each driver was ready. He walked back slowly, consulted briefly with another official. Then he turned, hesitated a second, and, leaping into the air, brought down the flag. There was a snarl from the pack of cars and they sped forward, engines roaring. Woody caught one glimpse of Rocky in the Mark II. She was neck and neck with a Jag, and before they disappeared around the first bend she had a slight overlap on it and had taken the outside position.

Woody turned to Worm. "She's chewed off one Jag anyway," he said. And he added fervently, "I hope nothing goes wrong."

Woody had agreed with Rocky to give her the number of each lap, her position, and her lap time. The first lap he could time her on was the second. The stop watch showed two minutes and fifty seconds for the two-and-a-half-mile lap. The Mark II was in seventh place, but nobody had set a real hot pace yet.

"I'm glad she's not pushing it," said Woody.

"What do ye mean not pushing it?" demanded Worm. "She knocks off three cars in two laps and you say she's not pushing it?" Worm looked nervous. Woody guessed that his fears were more for the car than the driver. He had a great love of automobiles.

Rocky held her position during the next four laps, but the pace of the whole pack had increased. Lap time was now two minutes and forty seconds. The cars were spread out in clusters over the track so that there were actually several races going on in the same event. Rocky was in the second of these clusters and still obviously nursing the Mark II.

Woody marked a big 5 on his blackboard and a lap time of two minutes and forty seconds and held it up as Rocky came into view on the tenth lap. She was in fourth place now, for the Cunningham which had been ahead of her had retired with brake trouble.

"Now she'll really start moving," Woody said. "If she's smart, she'll move up to third, hold it, and then take over the lead in the tenth lap." He realized that this was his way of racing, but Rocky's style was different. She just kept going, passing cars whenever she could and not leaving victory or defeat to the eight or nine minutes of the last three laps.

It was frustrating to be kept at the pits and not be able to see what was happening at other points. But the announcer filled in the blanks for them, and now his voice came excitedly over the loud-speaker.

"Keep your eyes on Rocky Randolph in number six," he said. "She's been battling Jean Salvatori's Ferrari for the last two laps. Rocky's driving a car completely new to the country—the Mark II, Black Tiger. Here it is. . . . Rocky Randolph has passed the Ferrari and

Betty Wisdom's D-Model Jag on the hairpin. Hello! Looks like trouble! No! Betty Wisdom looked as though she was going to spin out, but she regained control. Now it's Chris Madden's Ferrari, number twelve, first, Hazel Winter in a Jaguar second, and Rocky Randolph in the new Mark II, Black Tiger, third. With nine minutes to go, it's still anybody's race, but the Black Tiger, Mark II, looks good, real good."

"Holy cow," said Woody when Rocky sped by again. "Two minutes and thirty seconds! That's an average of sixty miles an hour on a track with two hairpins, four right angles, and a whole flock of S-bends. Boy, they must be pouring on the coal on the straightaway."

Worm said nothing. He had his hands clasped before him, his head down, and appeared to be saying his prayers.

"What's bothering you?" Woody asked.

Worm closed his eyes tight and said nothing for a second, then he opened them and said, "She'll have two gallons of gas left at the end of the race."

"Cripes," said Woody, "you figuring gas consumption at a time like this?"

"Aye," said Worm. "No sense carrying more gas than you need in a short race."

Woody turned to the race again. The announcer gave the positions on the far side of the track. Rocky's was still unchanged. Suddenly there was a roar from the crowd and a few seconds later the cars stormed into view around a bend.

"She's second," cried Woody. "Second! Boy, she's

gonna win this race. First race for the Mark II and she'll win it."

There was but one more lap to go, but Woody's hopes were not fufilled. The results were Chris Madden's Ferrari first and Rocky Randolph in the Black Tiger, Mark II, second.

But this result was in itself magnificent. The Mark II had proved its pedigree and ability in its first race. It had been a tough race with average speeds, as the announcer said, far higher than expected in a ladies' event.

"She's terrific," said Rocky, taking off her goggles. "Gave me no bad moments at all. She'll do things on corners you just haven't a right to expect of any car. It gives you a weird feeling. You have to deliberately refrain from braking when you want to, out of fairness to the car. It's kind of scary keeping your foot on the accelerator when everybody else is braking—scary but real fun. You'll find out."

Worm checked the gas tank with a dipstick he had calibrated himself. "Two gallons," he announced proudly.

"How the heck did you figure it?" asked Woody. "How did you know what her gas consumption would be with fuel injection and everything?"

"Ye'll find a whole chapter on fuel consumption and air to gasoline ratios in Davie's *Principles and Problems of Internal Combustion Engines*," said Worm. "There's nothing about automobiles that isn't tae be found in yon book."

"Heck," said Woody, "I looked in the front of it and

it was printed in nineteen-twenty. What did they know about fuel injection in those days?"

"Laddie," said Worm, "the first automobile that was ever invented, back somewhere in the sixteen hundreds, I believe, used fuel injection."

"You're kidding," said Woody. "They hadn't even thought of an automobile in those days."

"Oh yes, they had," said Worm. "A Dutch carpenter made one and he used fuel injection." He screwed the cap back on the gas tank and added, "The fuel he used was gunpowder and the engine blew up."

There were two more events for cars under fifteen hundred ccs, stock and modified, before the next race in which Woody was to drive the Black Tiger. That left something more than an hour for servicing the car, talking over the previous race with Rocky, picking up some pointers on the track, and answering questions of a score or more people who dropped by the pit to inspect the Black Tiger.

Woody felt that in fairness to Rocky he should answer all questions in detail, even though he would have preferred to have a little more time to himself before the race. After all, Rocky's livelihood depended on sales. The interest was keen, although there was a certain amount of reservation among the inquirers.

Woody knew whence that came. The Black Tiger, Mark I, had had a bad name at one time as a killer. It had ended its career with a wreck which Woody knew was not the car's fault. But nobody was going to put down sixty-five hundred dollars for the Mark II until it had been shown to be both a fast car and a safe car.

The hour's respite went by surprisingly fast. Woody ate a sandwich and drank a Coke, gassed the Mark II, checked the tires, brakes, and oil, and then the announcer said over the loud-speaker, "Cars for event number seven please proceed to the starting area."

Woody was already seated behind the wheel and Rocky climbed in beside him. If he was to beat her record, he'd have to come out first against some of the toughest competition on the West Coast, including his old friends Kurt Kreuger and Dave Kingston. He remembered the inquiry into his driving and said to himself, "The main thing is to get the feel of the car and not do anything reckless."

Woody looked around him. There were twenty-eight cars in the pack and he was positioned twenty-fifth. There was a lot of pedigree iron ahead of him to pass. And he had just an hour from start to finish to do it in.

He glanced around at the cockpit of the Mark II and toward the sleek hood ahead.

"Baby," he said, "you gotta learn to fly."

7   WOODY ALWAYS had a great sense of loneliness in the few minutes immediately preceding the start of a race. He was a veteran of sports-car racing now and yet this sense of utter isolation while he waited for the starter's green flag to fall had never left him. Others, he knew, felt the same way. The sounds of the engines around seemed unreal and remote to him. When he smiled at another driver, he was conscious that this was not really a smile, but a twisting of his face which had become a kind of mask. His palms always sweated slightly and his breath came in quick gasps.

He felt all these sensations now as, leaning slightly over the side of the Mark II, he watched the starter, a slim little puppet some hundred yards ahead with a green flag under his arm.

It occurred to Woody, as it had many times before, that at the start of a race he hated the starter. He seemed an utterly callous individual deriving pleasure from drawing out these moments of pre-race anxiety to their fullest.

The Ferrari ahead of him revved suddenly and irritatingly and as a reflex Woody touched the accelerator of the Mark II. There was a "whoom" of power from the six-cylinder engine located a little more than a foot behind him. Then the green flag fluttered aloft for a second, then fell, and they were off.

Despite his anxieties, Woody had worked out his tactics for the first few seconds of the race. Woody had cramped his wheels hard right, before the start and now swept past the Ferrari. The Mark II was soon part of a milling mob of cars, dimly seen through their own exhaust and dust, seeking a slot to get through the pack in these first few precious seconds.

Woody didn't do badly, passing three cars in the first minute of acceleration, so that he was no longer positioned twenty-fifth but twenty-second. He had hardly got into high before the pack slowed for the first corner, a broad right-angle bend. Woody started to take an outside position and then remembered the Mark II's remarkable ability on corners. He stayed in the middle of the road, steadied the Mark II, dropped her down a notch, and then poured the power to her. When he came around the corner, he had passed two other cars, a Jag and a Corvette.

"Better just find out something about the track for a couple of laps," Woody told himself. "No sense pushing the pace now." He was particularly worried about a hairpin in the northwest corner. It came at the end of half a mile of straightaway and was very tight and narrow. He'd have to drop into second for it—he knew that. What he didn't know was when he should shut off and just what the camber was on the corner. For three laps he contented himself with following the car ahead, studying the course.

The particular hairpin had a sort of groove at the end

of the paving on the near side of the corner. Everybody tried to get the right front wheel into this, to give them a hold against the force of inertia which sought to fling their cars wide around the curve. Woody did the same thing twice and noted that he was taking the corner at something less than thirty miles an hour. Furthermore, he was always blocked by the car ahead of him. To pass, he would have to desert the groove and take the hairpin on the outside.

He determined to try it. When he passed the pits on the next lap, he saw Worm holding up the blackboard. It said it was the eighth lap and he was now nineteenth. He was not conscious of having passed any cars and actually he hadn't. The others ahead had dropped out with trouble. His lap time was two minutes and forty seconds. It was time to start warming things up.

Woody had by now to some extent overcome his feeling of strangeness toward the Mark II. He felt the car to be part of himself, an extension as it were of his own brain and limbs. He was reasonably confident of what it would do on this particular track. He pushed the accelerator down all the way for the first time in the race and grinned as his torso was thrust back against the seat and the Mark II leaped forward.

A Cunningham ahead moved over to shoot bend number one, a right angle, which was somewhat narrow in the throat. Woody passed on the inside, saw the taillight of a red Jag wink for a second, and still kept his foot on the throttle.

He reached the corner wheel to wheel with the Jag, stepped on the brake, changed down, and set up a power drift. He had three feet on the Jag when they were two-thirds of the way around the bend and he hit the accelerator hard and straightened his front wheels. The Jag drifted behind him, and Woody slipped into high for four hundred yards of straight.

The same tactics, shutting off late and taking the inside track, served him well on three successive turns. He experimented with the hairpin, taking it wide instead of shooting for the inside groove. He passed no one but lost no distance. And the Mark II held the road without a whimper. When he passed the racing pits again, Worm's blackboard told him his lap time was two minutes and thirty seconds, and he was now twelfth.

"The hairpin's the place to chew off a few," he said to himself. "They're all going round like blind men playing follow the leader." He was beginning to feel a sense of elation, of enormous well-being and confidence. And when he came to the hairpin he delayed braking until he was upon the last shutoff mark, changed swiftly down to third, and then second, took the outside lane, and hit the accelerator.

From the engine behind came a huge roar of power and he heard his tires shriek. He eased the accelerator a little to control the spin of the rear wheels, and pulled the wheel over to the right. He caught a glimpse of people melting away from the snow fence on the far side. But the Mark II was in complete control. It broadsided around snarling and fighting against the tons of inertia which strove to sweep it off the asphalt. Then the corner was rounded and Woody fled down the straight. He believed he had passed two cars, a Mercedes and a

Jaguar. Actually he had passed three. And the crowd was going wild. He could hear the roar from them as he streaked by, the sound fleeing past his head. He shot a series of S-bends, cutting tangents across them, and was past the racing pits without time even to glance at the board Worm held up.

He made three more laps, and knew that now was the crisis of the race. There were but nine minutes left—nine minutes and three cars ahead and one of them a Mercedes, another a red-hot factory Kurtis-Chrysler, with a 4.9 Ferrari Mexico leading. They represented, Woody knew, about the toughest competition he was likely to come up against in any road race anywhere for quite a while.

He trailed them for one lap, crowding the Kurtis in third place and watching its cornering characteristics and the style of the driver. He was of the wide-angle-of-entry school and Woody grinned. With the greater stability of the Mark II he would be able to get between the Kurtis and the inside of the corner and slip around. On any given corner he would have no more than a couple of seconds to do this. He chose the right angle immediately after the start-finish line. The Kurtis braked and Woody kept going. He felt the muscles of his stomach tighten as he slipped alongside the American-built car, braked, changed down, and then revved the Mark II. If anything went wrong now he'd broadside right into the other car in a tangle of steel and whirling wheels.

Nothing went wrong. The driver of the Kurtis was surprised by the maneuver. He had been concentrating on the corner, on cutting in close to it from a wide angle and now he found the space occupied by the Mark II. There was nothing for him to do but hit his brakes, and Woody was by, moving up to the third spot with the Mercedes ahead of him.

The Mercedes was fighting it out with the lead car, the Ferrari, seeking every opportunity to get by. Kurt Kreuger was in the Ferrari and Woody knew he was a wizard at holding the lead position. He had nerves of steel and never let up blocking the car behind him for a moment. He never left any loopholes. The three cars roared through the gantlets of S-bends with scarcely a foot between them. Woody couldn't get by the Mercedes. Every time he tried to sneak by, the car was there blocking him. They went round a switchback—a greater than right-angle bend—without any change in their order, and flung down the straight headed for the hairpin. On the straight Woody snapped into high and drew abreast of the Mercedes. The landscape merged into a gray blur. He was conscious that the Mercedes was slipping behind him a little but still had an overlap on him. Then the hairpin leaped at them out of the distance with the Mark II on the outside.

The Mercedes braked and dropped back, losing its overlap. Woody saw the brake lights wink on Kurt's Ferrari, and glanced at his speedometer. He was clocking one hundred and thirty-five. He hit the brakes, clutch, and accelerator, and changed down to third and then second. He had his toe on the brake pedal and his heel on the accelerator and pressed the two. The Mark II's engine roared at seven thousand rpm and his rear tires screamed, spinning on the tarmac.

"Now," said Woody to himself, and moved the wheel over to take the turn. He and Kurt went into the hairpin together, the Mark II on the outside, Kurt riding the groove on the inside of the bend.

They were still together with the Mark II beside but slightly to the rear of the Ferrari when they got around the acute angle of the hairpin.

Woody took a chance. He should hold the Mark II in second a couple of seconds more to gain the additional bite needed by the straining rear wheels. Instead he declutched, changed into third and hit the accelerator. There was a sickening moment when the Mark II swayed over to the left, her rear wheels faltering. Then she took off like a bullet. Kurt had changed up, too, but too late. The Mark II swept ahead, and Woody slipped into high. The gap between the two cars increased from a matter of a few inches to a foot, then two feet. Woody pulled the Mark II over and gave it all the power it had.

He was not conscious of how he retained the lead in the last lap. He had no clear plan for doing so except to keep going at full bore. Later Kurt said, ruefully, that he spoiled every corner for him by staying inside so that Kurt could not shoot it properly. But stay ahead he did, and as he passed the finish line, he was the first to receive the checkered flag.

He had won by three seconds!

Worm's face was flushed with excitement when Woody drove into his pit after a slowdown lap. "Mon," he said, "you drove like Jack the Bear." Jack the Bear was the legendary figure of sports-car drivers, as Paul Bunyan was of lumbermen. Woody grinned.

"You can't lose in a car like this," he exulted. "I wasn't worried about losing power on any corner. There were rpms to throw away."

Rocky grabbed Woody's head and planted a kiss firmly on his mouth.

Just then Kurt Kreuger came up, his face grave.

"What's the matter, Kurt?" asked Woody, genuinely concerned.

"Aw, for cripes' sake," said Kurt. "That guy in the Kurtis, Mathews is his name, is entering a protest."

"A protest?" cried Woody, Rocky, and Worm together.

"Yes," said Kurt glumly. "He's one of those gentleman drivers who don't like to lose. He is protesting you on the grounds of reckless driving. Says you deliberately charged him on a corner and he had to get out of the way to let you by. Either that or be killed."

"What the heck's the matter with that guy?" said Woody. "I took the corner on the inside. He was going to shoot in from way over. That's all. I could do it because the Black Tiger will corner tight. I knew the car could do it. . . ."

Just then the announcer's voice came over the loudspeakers. "There's been a correction on the results of the last race," he said soberly. "A protest has been entered against the driver who finished first, Woody Hartford. We are not able to give the official results until a hearing has been held.

"Will Woody Hartford, the driver of the Mark II, Black Tiger, number six, please come to the judges' stand."

Woody slowly took off his helmet and climbed out of the Mark II. He looked grimly at Rocky and Worm and Kurt and then walked over in the direction of the judges' stand near the start-finish line. All three went with him.

8 THE PROTEST against Woody on grounds of reckless and dangerous driving was not investigated at the judges' stand on the day of the race. Woody had been asked to go over there to see Jim Withers, president of the Southern California Sports Car Association, meet Mathews, who had protested him, and see whether the matter couldn't be straightened out between them.

The meeting with Mathews was nervous and tense. Mathews was highly excited and talked volubly and threw accusations at Woody right and left. He was flanked by his pit crew, who kept silent and did not seem wholeheartedly in support of their driver.

"You ought to be ruled off Southern California tracks," said Mathews, waving a finger under Woody's nose and not waiting for an introduction. "If I hadn't given way to you on that bend, I'd have been killed. You're not a driver. You're a man-killer."

Woody was speechless under this outburst. But Worm wasn't. "Mon," he said to Mathews, his Aberdeen accent thickened by anger, "why dinna ye buy yerself a scooter and keep tae the sidewalk? Ye've no right oot on the road there playing wi' the big boys."

"Who the devil are you?" demanded Mathews.

"Ye wouldna understand," replied Worm with heavy sarcasm. "I'm a *man*. . . ."

"Gentlemen, gentlemen," said Withers. "Please control yourselves. Mr. Mathews has lodged a complaint of recklessness against Mr. Hartford. I brought you together to see whether this thing has to be investigated officially. We have had no reports from the track officials about recklessness on Mr. Hartford's part."

"They must be blind," said Mathews, and Withers winced. Flagmen on the race tracks risk their lives for no pay, and were anything but blind. "I tell you this jerk nearly killed me."

By now Woody had recovered from his initial shock. "Listen," he said to Mathews, "you can protest me if you want, but don't stand there and call me a jerk or I'll chop you down to size."

"Please, please," interrupted Withers. "Let's forget about personalities. The issue at stake is one of track safety and has nothing to do with your personal feelings about each other.

"Do you wish to make your charge formally," he continued, turning to Mathews, "and have an official investigation made?"

One of Mathews' pit men took him by the arm and led him away. They had a private talk, and Mathews returned, not quite so excited.

"Well," he said, "I don't know about a formal investigation. It takes a lot of time and trouble, and I have to get back East in a couple of days . . ."

"One moment," said Woody. "The announcement

has gone out to all the fans and other drivers and pit crews that you have protested me. There's either going to be an official investigation or you are going to withdraw your charges, and say so over that microphone." He pointed to the mike in the judges' stand.

"I'll withdraw nothing," said Mathews, belligerent again.

"Then I insist upon an investigation," said Woody. He looked at Withers. "I think it is only fair that you tell them over the loud-speakers that I've insisted on an official investigation. My reputation as a driver is at stake here."

Withers nodded, and Woody and the others returned to their pit. On the way back Woody wondered whether he had done the right thing. There'd be a lot of discussion and printed comment over the matter. It might have been better to let the whole thing blow over. This meant two investigations into his driving methods in two months, and whatever the verdict, it might result in his getting a bad name.

Matters were not helped in the couple of days that elapsed before the investigation was held at the same hotel as the previous inquiry. Edghill ran a story about the matter. He was himself noncommittal, but he reminded his readers that this was the second inquiry into Woody's fitness as a racing driver in a matter of a few weeks. Woody felt he could have done without that remark.

His father said nothing, and Woody at times wished that he would make some comment, whatever it was.

His silence seemed tantamount to a suspicion that the charges might be true. Worm and Rocky proved stanch allies. But a real source of trouble was Mary Jane.

The difficulty with Mary Jane came the Monday following the races, when Woody had a date to take her to dinner. Woody, sick at heart, told her what had happened and was hardly prepared for her reaction.

She plunged right into a denunciation of sports-car racing and in particular of his participation in it. She said she was sick and tired of all Woody's weekends being booked with races or preparations for them. She returned to the old theme of saving money for furniture and a down payment on a house if they were ever going to be married. And she wound up with a demand that Woody choose between racing and her.

"I'm not going to play second fiddle to a sports car and a scheming brunette," flared Mary Jane, thoroughly aroused.

"Scheming brunette?" echoed Woody, mystified.

"You know who I mean," said Mary Jane. "That Rocky Randolph."

"Rocky's nothing more than a darn good friend and a darn good driver," said Woody. "And I'm real lucky that she lets me drive the Mark II."

"I'll say she's a darn good friend," stormed Mary Jane. "So good, in fact, that she thinks nothing of kissing you in public."

"Kissing me in public?" Woody repeated. Then he recalled the victory kiss Rocky had given him right after the race. There had been a picture of it in the papers.

"Oh, for goodness' sakes, Mary Jane," he said. "That was nothing."

"Nothing!" flared Mary Jane. "It didn't look like nothing to me." All the suppressed jealousy which she had felt for Rocky, who shared so much of Woody's life, now came tumbling out and could not be withheld. "We're supposed to be engaged, Woody Hartford. I don't know whether you realize it, but that means that we're supposed to be planning to get married. And you spend more of your time with that Rocky hussy than you do with me.

"Well, perhaps it's all my fault. I've put up with it, and that has encouraged you. But now I've stopped putting up with it. You don't have to worry about dates with me interfering with your sports-car activities. I'm setting you free! Our engagement is off! You can go your own way and I'll go mine."

She stormed on, repeating words and sentences vaguely familiar to Woody. He realized that thousands of other engaged couples had gone through the same scene and the same recriminations, and condemnations had been used in the same words. But now they were being applied to him and he was appalled and at the same time stunned by an overwhelming sense of injustice.

Mary Jane concluded by taking the engagement ring off her finger and throwing it on the table before them. "There you are, Mr. Woody Hartford," she said, "you're free to run right round to your friend Rocky now." And she swept out of the restaurant. Woody stared at the engagement ring for a few seconds, then picked it up and put it in his pocket and followed her out.

He drove Mary Jane home in silence and wasn't even conscious whether he said good night to her or not.

The date of the hearing was set for the following Friday, and Worm was more indignant about it than Woody. Whenever the name of Mathews was mentioned he had a hard time controlling himself. "In my day," he said, "we'd have gone over to that guy's pit and given him a working over with a wrench. It would help to make a man of him."

Rocky was horrified. There were a number of events in Worm's racing past in Europe of a bloody character at which she only guessed. "You mean you'd beat someone up with a wrench?" she asked.

"Weel," said Worm, "he'd have the same chance to beat me up. There's a few of them tried," and his face took on a faraway look and a smile of fond recollection. Worm had served his apprenticeship in automobiles in factories of Glasgow and Coventry, in an era not noted for gentility among automobile workers.

The investigation itself proved something of a fiasco. It lasted less than an hour and it was evident from the start that Mathews hadn't a leg to stand on.

He tried to prove that Woody had deliberately attempted to ram him on the corner. There had been cases in the past of drivers losing their tempers and doing such a thing. But in all such instances there was plenty of supporting evidence from other drivers and from the flagmen. In Mathews' case, he could find no one to support his story, although he himself stuck to it. He was coming for the corner, he maintained, and was ahead of the Mark II when Woody had rammed straight at him. To avoid a crash, he had had to brake hard, his car had gone momentarily out of control, and he had avoided turning over only as a result of good luck.

"This guy Hartford already has a bad reputation," Mathews concluded. "Other drivers would have complained against him in the past, but they seem to be scared."

"We're considering the present incident and not hearsay based on other people's opinions," said Withers sternly. "Are there any of the other drivers who were near at the time of this alleged attempt to ram who will bear out your story?"

"No," said Mathews, "they're all scared of saying anything because they don't want to be called bad sports."

"It seems to me that there may be a question of bad sportsmanship involved here," Withers said half to himself, "but I'm not prepared to say who is guilty of it." And he looked very hard at Mathews.

Woody then gave his own version. He said he'd taken the corner tight because the Mark II was very stable and could corner safely from the inside position. He'd certainly cut into the slot that the Kurtis was headed for, but that was perfectly legitimate in his view. He knew of nothing in racing rules to prevent a driver taking advantage of any loophole offered him.

Kurt Kreuger, although he couldn't testify about this particular incident since he had been ahead, said that when Woody passed him on the hairpin, he did it by superb driving and complete knowledge of his car's characteristics.

"I saw nothing reckless about his driving that day," he said, "and I saw plenty of it. He beat me." The flagmen said the Mark II was taking corners close but was always under control. They had no bad reports to make and none had for a moment considered black-flagging Woody (that is, ordering him off the track) during any part of the race.

Withers consulted for a few minutes with the other officials present and then gave the board's decision: the charge of reckless driving was unsubstantiated and in the board's view completely without foundation. Then Withers added, "I hope this present inquiry will not result in Mr. Hartford's getting a bad name as a result of a lot of ill-considered talk. He leaves this room completely exonerated and in the view of the board is the kind of driver who is always welcome at our events."

Woody knew that these remarks were addressed to the members of the press as well as the other drivers present. The newspaper reports the following day stated that Woody had been cleared of the charge. But the very fact that there had been two investigations into his driving still caused a great deal of comment in Southern California racing circles.

Two camps developed—one led by Mathews, who said, though not openly, that Woody was a hazard on any race track. The other camp, led by Worm and Kurt Kreuger and Dave Kingston, maintained that he was one of the best of the younger crop of sports-car drivers.

Worm went further than that. He let it be known that he was prepared to settle any differences of opinion on the matter Glasgow style, by which Woody understood him to mean with a heavy wrench.

9

ONE DAY several weeks later Worm McNess surveyed the crankcase of a Bentley roadster which had been brought to him for a complete overhaul. The car had only forty thousand miles on its speedometer, and yet it had broken down completely. The crankcase was full of a heavy, thick, black goo, not unlike road oil.

"Woody," he said, "come and take a look at this."

Woody went over and they peered solemnly into the crankcase together. Worm dipped a forefinger into the goo, lifted it up, and watched the thick liquid slop slowly off it.

"I wonder what he used for oil," Worm asked solemnly.

"I'll bet I know what happened," said Woody. "That guy read somewhere that lubricating oil never breaks down in an automobile engine and so there's never any need to change it. All you got to do is keep filling up the crankcase. So he never changed the oil."

Worm, very sensitive to what happened to automobile engines which he considered living and delicate beings, paled. "It doesn't even look to me as though he put in any new oil," he said with horror. "Here, call him up and ask him. I wouldna trust myself to speak to him on the telephone." He gave Woody a name and telephone number, and Woody made the call.

"The gentleman says that he didn't put any new oil in the car because he was told when he bought the Bentley that Bentleys don't use any oil," he reported back.

Worm sat down on a rickety stool with a groan. He covered his face with his hands, and Woody was reminded of a poem he'd read about a Cossack grieving over the death of his horse.

"Tae think that imbeciles like that are allowed tae drive aroond the streets after paying two dollars for a license," he said. The whole engine had frozen solid for lack of lubrication and would have to be rebuilt.

"What kind of work does this guy do?" Woody asked.

"He doesna work," said Worm. "He owns a big oil company. Oil wells and a seventeen-thousand-dollar car, and he was too mean to pay the price of having his oil changed." He shook his head in anguish and mystification.

It was now three weeks since the investigation and the Black Tiger had not been raced since then. It stood on the lot opposite Worm's garage, still a center of interest and inquiry. But so far no one had placed an order.

Woody, looking at the ruined Bentley, wondered whether he couldn't get the owner interested in a Black Tiger. Then he debated whether he should. He was torn between the desire for a sale and love of the car which the Bentley owner might readily ruin. He had a date with Rocky that night and decided he would mention the matter then.

Woody's date with Rocky was not to be a twosome. It was not even a romantic date. Worm was to be present and Rocky's Aunt Babs. She had been down in San Diego packing their furniture, for Rocky and she were to move from San Diego to Hermosa Beach to be nearer their business. So the occasion was a reunion with Babs and a belated celebration of the Mark II's recent victory. And Worm was going because he liked Woody and Rocky and also because, though he wouldn't admit it, he like Rocky's Aunt Babs. He had met her only a couple of times but he had told Woody she was a sensible woman. That was small enough praise, but it was the biggest compliment Worm had paid any woman in the four years Woody had known him.

The only conveyance for this double date was Worm's venerable Dodge, now overhauled and in Worm's opinion as good as new. Woody would have said, had he dared, that even new, the 1928 Dodge hadn't been very good, but he kept quiet. The car, in which it was necessary to sit bolt upright as one did on a straight-back chair, was hardly suitable to the occasion, but both Babs and Rocky were delighted to ride in it. Babs endeared herself to Worm immediately by saying she loved the Dodge because it reminded her of the wonderful cars she used to ride around in when she was a girl. She was rewarded by a discussion of the history of the automobile and a beginner's course in the rules governing automobile engines with many references to Davie's *Principles and Problems of Internal Combustion Engines*.

This conversation went on during the soup, and Babs

didn't seem to wilt under it. Woody, however, took pity on her, and seeking to save her, mentioned the wealthy owner of the Bentley. "He might be a prospective customer for an authentic copy of the world's greatest sports car—the Black Tiger, Mark II," he said.

Worm put his fork down in horror. "Mon," he said, "have ye no heart? Didna ye see wi' yer own eyes the pitiable condition he'd reduced yon Bentley to? The thought of it puts me off my food." But he nonetheless picked up his fork, and using it in his left hand in the European fashion, speared a piece of steak, two french fried potatoes, and some creamed cauliflower on it, conveying the whole load to his mouth.

When he had done this, and approved of the taste, he was troubled for a moment by the thought that he might be pushing aside a considerable amount of money due someone else. Money, in Worm's view, as always, was a commodity to be treated with the greatest respect.

"On the other hand," he said, "a man can be too cautious about who he sells cars to. There's no society for the prevention of cruelty to automobiles."

"If there were, we'd both be a lot worse off," said Woody. Rocky was interested in the Bentley owner whose name was Tanner. Woody said that if she liked he'd sound him out as a prospective customer, and bring him over to Rocky's lot to look over the Black Tiger. Rocky agreed that it was worth while doing.

The following Monday Mr. Tanner came in person to Worm's garage. He was a pudgy little man, pink-faced, bald-headed, and wore an Italian-silk suit which must have cost around two hundred dollars. He arrived in a chauffeur-driven Cadillac and had, to Worm's surprise, a photographer with him. His manner was brisk.

"What would you say of the condition of my Bentley?" he asked Worm.

Worm was no diplomat. "Ye've ruined the engine entirely," he said.

"Excellent," said Mr. Tanner, positively beaming. "And how did I manage to ruin the engine?"

"Ye drove it forty thousand miles without an oil change," he snapped.

"Ah, it was more than that. Much more than that. I don't mean the distance. The forty thousand miles is correct. But I didn't even add any oil. The oil in that crankcase is what was in the car when I bought it. Not a drop has been added." His round pink face broke into an unexpected smile. "You think I'm crazy, don't you?" he asked.

"I do," said Worm.

"Well, I'm not as crazy as you think," said Mr. Tanner. "The Bentley is one of the finest engines produced in England, is it not? And this piece of automobile craftsmanship has been ruined through improper lubrication—a classic example of losing the ship for a ha'porth of tar.

"Now," he continued, "you know that I am the proprietor of a number of oil wells, and I am also a major shareholder in a very big oil company. I'm going to use that car as advertising. I'm going to have pictures taken of the condition of the engine—plain pictures and microphotographs. I want those pictures to show how every part of this fine piece of machinery, produced by leading craftsmen, has been utterly ruined by my refusal to change the oil.

"Those pictures I intend to use in a nationwide advertising campaign to impress on drivers the need for constant oil changes in their cars. There has been a falling off in sales of lubricating oil recently, due to a widespread belief that frequent oil changes are not needed, since oil does not break down in an automobile engine. That story has cost us heavily and ignores the fact that oil gets dirty and automobile filters will not clean it thoroughly.

"In short, for seventeen thousand dollars, which is the cost of that car, I have obtained a classic example of what happens to an automobile when the oil is not changed frequently. That will be worth at least a hundred thousand dollars to myself and the companies in which I am interested."

Worm gasped. "Ye mean you deliberately ruined this engine?" he asked.

"I did," Mr. Tanner replied.

Worm shuddered.

"But in so doing I may well save the engines of thousands of family cars now being driven in the United States," continued Mr. Tanner, with all the zeal of a missionary. "This photographer is to take as many pictures as he wants of every part of that engine which has been ruined by lack of lubrication. Give him every facility. Naturally I will pay for any inconvenience involving yourself."

He turned to go, smug, contented, smiling slightly,

and Worm and Woody were so astounded that Mr. Tanner had reached the door of his Cadillac, which the chauffeur held open for him, before Woody remembered the Mark II.

"Mr. Tanner," he said, hurrying after him.

Tanner turned.

"Just a minute," said Woody. "You're pretty interested in cars, aren't you, Mr. Tanner?" It was not the best sales approach, but it was the best he could devise at the moment.

"As consumers of gasoline and lubricating oil, I am vitally interested in them," said Mr. Tanner.

"I wonder if you've got the time to look at absolutely the latest thing in sports cars," he said. "It isn't far from here—right across the road, in fact. There's only one of them in the country."

"Sports cars?" asked Mr. Tanner.

"Yes," said Woody. And then he had a flash of sheer inspiration. "We use gas and oil in huge quantities just to run races," he said. "It's a growing outlet for your products." He didn't mention that the gas and oil used on race tracks was supplied free by the Mobilgas people.

Mr. Tanner produced a slim gold watch from the vest of his gleaming silk suit. "I have twenty minutes," he said. "I would like to see this car."

Woody hurried him over to the Black Tiger lot.

10

MR. TANNER displayed an encouraging interest in the Black Tiger, Mark II. He didn't know a great deal about automobile engines, and Woody was afraid he didn't appreciate the sales talk he gave him on the Mark II's fuel-injection system, the principle of the opposed cylinders, the titanium-alloy block, and other features which the Mark II possessed.

But nevertheless he was interested, and particularly in the fact that the oil was changed every two thousand miles. Woody told him he believed the Mark II would take over the place in sports-car racing now occupied by the Jag and the Ferrari.

"I haven't seen any of them around," said Mr. Tanner. "How many of them have you sold?"

"None," said Woody. "This car represents the first shipment. It's the only one in the country. You could be the first person to own the Mark II in the United States. It would be kinda like having a car built specially for you—for a while."

"The car looks very flimsy to me," said Mr. Tanner.

Woody expounded on the ruggedness of the construction and on the beating which the engine was designed to take in road racing. He gave the Mark II's record, two races with a second in one and a first in the other.

Mr. Tanner seemed impressed by this. Then he said, "I'm not interested in driving a car in races. These road races you talk of are around a track of something under three miles and last for about an hour. That is a test of a car's endurance over a short period of maximum effort. What interests me is a car which has the same kind of endurance for long periods over several hundred miles."

"The Mark II will stand up to any kind of road condition in any kind of weather for any kind of distance," Woody said fervently.

"Are you quite sure?" asked Mr. Tanner, the suggestion of a twinkle in his eyes.

"Certainly I'm sure," said Woody.

"What's the most grueling road race in the world?" asked Mr. Tanner.

"The Mexican Road Race," said Woody. "It's about two thousand miles, full bore, over every kind of road surface, from the Guatemala border clean through Mexico to the United States border."

"Indeed," said Mr. Tanner. "That's very interesting." He took out the slim gold watch again, looked at it, and said, "Well, I must be getting along. Remember to give the photographer every facility." He offered Woody a small plump hand and crossed the road to his Cadillac.

"What did he say?" asked Rocky, coming out of the office. She had kept in the background because men don't like to be told about cars by women, because they automatically assume they know nothing about the subject.

"He didn't say anything," said Woody, dejected. "He

just asked a few questions, wanted to know the world's toughest road race, and then took off."

"Oh, well," said Rocky, "there'll be a customer someday. It's bound to be tough in the beginning. The banks will handle only fifty per cent of the purchase price and that means that a buyer has to put up three thousand in cash. I wish we had enough money to handle part of the financing ourselves. But Babs and I are broke. All our money's tied up."

"There'll be a break sometime," said Woody, and went back to help Worm.

The following day there was a phone call to Worm's garage from Mr. Tanner. Worm answered the telephone and assured him that the photographer was taking a lot of pictures and would have plenty more to take.

"Let me speak to that young assistant of yours," said Mr. Tanner. "What's his name?"

"Woody Hartford," said Worm, and called Woody to the telephone.

"Mr. Hartford?" asked Mr. Tanner. "I want you up at my house this evening at six-thirty. If you have some other appointment, break it. This is more important to you." He gave an address on Beverly Canyon Drive in Beverly Hills and hung up.

Woody, not quite sure that all this had happened to him, told Worm.

"The mon's clean out of his head," said Worm sourly. "He ought to be in an asylum."

"Might have something to do with the Black Tiger," said Woody. "I'll go and tell Rocky."

Just then the telephone rang again. "You answer it," said Worm. "It'll be him calling to say the appointment's off. He's going to spend the evening wi' the man in the moon."

But the phone call was not from Mr. Tanner. It was from Mary Jane—a Mary Jane repentant over her quarrel with Woody and worried that he had made no move toward reconciliation in the past three weeks.

She inquired how he was and whether his broken collarbone and ribs had mended and what he was doing, and to all this Woody replied that he was feeling fine and just working as usual. "Gee, I'm sorry about our quarrel," said Mary Jane suddenly. "I really am sorry, Woody. I've missed you."

Woody said he was sorry, too, and had missed her. But he said it with some caution.

"Can you come around this evening?" asked Mary Jane.

"Gee, I wish I could," said Woody, "but I've got an appointment." He explained about the mysterious Mr. Tanner and Mary Jane sounded disappointed.

"Is Rocky going with you?" Mary Jane asked.

"No," said Woody. "Just me. That was all he asked for."

"Well, perhaps you can come around tomorrow," said Mary Jane, and that ended the conversation.

At five o'clock that evening Mr. Tanner's chauffeur-driven Cadillac rolled into Worm's service station. Woody was still in his coveralls, getting ready to change and go home and clean up. The chauffeur handed him a note. It was in a large, bold handwriting and read as follows:

"I am sending my car to bring you to my house. It occurs to me that you may not be the only party interested in that car you showed me. I forget the name of it. Please bring with you any other persons connected with its sales. This is important. Tobias Tanner."

"Cripes, I'd better take Rocky," said Woody, and raced across the road to tell her.

Rocky was delighted. "I'll bet he's going to buy a car," she said.

"Well, we'll soon find out," said Woody. "Put on your best bib and tucker. I'll tell the chauffeur to drive you home and I'll meet you over there. It's only a couple of blocks. Be ready by six?"

"Sure," said Rocky. "But why don't I drive up in the Mark II? He might want to look it over again."

The chauffeur turned this down. "Mr. Tanner's instructions," he said, "were that I was to take you and whoever else was to come in his car. He might be offended if you arrived in any other."

Woody shrugged. It was plain that Mr. Tanner was eccentric. But if he was a customer, that was good enough for Woody. He met Rocky, as agreed, at six o'clock. She wore a pale blue semi-formal and a necklace of jet mounted in silver. Woody suddenly realized that she was a real knockout and he wondered why he hadn't noticed this before. He felt a little awkward himself in a charcoal-gray suit. He was so used to coveralls that the jacket felt uncomfortable around his shoulders.

He helped Rocky into the back of the Cadillac and sat down beside her. Rocky called out "Hi," and waved to someone, and the Cadillac purred away from the sidewalk.

"Who was that?" asked Woody.

Rocky looked at him evenly. "Mary Jane," she said.

11 THE WORD "house" could not properly be used for the residence in Beverly Hills of Mr. Tobias Tanner. Mansion would have been more suitable. It lay in what must have been an acre of grounds, a building of pink and black, of cantilever construction, so that the greater part of the second floor jutted out over the ground floor without any visible support. And this second floor was not even square with the ground floor. It lay at an angle to it, and the impression was conveyed that one good push and the whole thing would collapse.

The exterior of this house, the brain child of one of the more advanced of California architects, was by no means its most remarkable feature. The place was full of surprises. In the living room into which Rocky and Woody were conducted by a butler there was a tree growing. It wasn't just a big bush in a concrete planter, but a huge cypress, its gnarled trunk twisting up through a floor of polished marble and exiting through a glass wall at one end of the living room.

The room itself was so big that its couches and chairs seemed like toys, and there were bearskin rugs lying about the floor as carelessly as throw rugs.

At one end of this fantastic living room was a fireplace. It was sunk below the floor in a kind of well, but this well was so wide that it could accommodate a circular couch down on the same level as the fireplace.

Thus, when Rocky and Woody entered, they saw neither the fire nor Mr. Tanner. He was sprawled below the level of the floor, on the circular couch, basking in the firelight.

"Ah, Mr. Hartford. Very kind of you to come," said Mr. Tanner, popping up suddenly from below the floor. He looked inquiringly at Rocky, and Woody introduced her as the agent for the Black Tiger Automobile Company in the United States and one of the major shareholders in the factory in Italy. They were invited to join the surprising Mr. Tanner down in the huge well-like area containing the fire.

"This," said Mr. Tanner, obviously very pleased with himself, "is entirely my own design, and results from the fact that in my youth I was a cowboy."

"A cowboy?" said Woody. He was astonished both by the statement and the fact that he couldn't connect punching cows with such an exotic fireplace.

"Yes," said Mr. Tanner. "I worked on a ranch in Wyoming for forty dollars a month when I was a boy of fifteen. One night I was caught out in a blizzard fifteen miles from the bunkhouse. I was two days in that blizzard and the determination came very strongly to me that one day I would build myself a fireplace which I could curl around, as it were, so that I need never be so cold again. This is the result. This whole room I call my Wyoming room. You have noticed the tree, no doubt.

There was such a tree nearby during those two nights I spent in the blizzard. I tried to get the precise tree for this room, but it had been removed. That cypress is a substitute."

He went on talking about a past which was so amazing it would be discounted as outrageous fiction if it were printed in a book. While punching cows he had noted several faults on the Wyoming uplands where there were oil seepages. He had quietly saved his money and bought this land. The resulting wells, heavy producers, were the initial source of his wealth.

There was little need for either Woody or Rocky to contribute much to the conversation. All that was required was to ask a question, and Mr. Tanner, apparently very pleased at the opportunity, took off on another story about his past. Woody guessed that he didn't often get a chance to talk at such length. Probably his business acquaintances and other friends had heard the same stories over and over again, and didn't care to listen. Woody guessed that for all his wealth Mr. Tanner was possibly a little lonely.

They were through dinner (served on a table of plate glass suspended from the ceiling) before Mr. Tanner turned to the reason for his invitation. "Young man," he said to Woody, "the last time we met, you were talking about this new sports car to me. By the way, what is the name of the car?"

"The Black Tiger, Mark II," said Woody.

"Well," continued Mr. Tanner, "you seem to believe that this is a car of a superior sort, and told me, I believe, that it would stand up under any kind of road condition. Then we discussed the Mexican Road Race."

"Yes," said Woody, and his heart was pounding.

"I have had my secretary make some inquiries about this Mexican Road Race," said Mr. Tanner. He reached into the inside pocket of his jacket and took out a leather-bound notebook with a large gold monogram on it. This he opened with his small, pudgy hands.

"What you have said about this road race appears to be quite correct. It is grueling in the extreme. Driving conditions range from tropical temperatures at sea level to near freezing ones in the mountains at ten thousand feet. Every kind of road surface is encountered.

"Now I want to make you a proposition. I have been thinking more about my advertising campaign in which I intend to show engine wear due to neglected lubrication of the Bentley. That is excellent as far as it goes. But advertising is best when it is positive.

"I want to follow up the series based on the Bentley with another showing what happens to the moving parts of an automobile engine when it has received a severe testing over all kinds of road conditions but has been given thoroughly efficient lubrication."

Rocky and Woody exchanged glances. They both suspected what Mr. Tanner was leading up to but were not sure.

"Of course," said Mr. Tanner, "I can obtain this kind of evidence in a variety of ways. I can obtain it by merely hiring a man to drive any stock automobile around the United States from coast to coast and border to border. But that has some drawbacks. There is the disadvantage of the speed limit imposed upon the driver. And it is not spectacular.

"Nothing is remembered by the public these days unless it is spectacular," he continued. "This is the age of spectacle. To be noticed at all, something must be astounding." He indicated with his hand the living room in which they were seated. Certainly neither Woody nor Rocky would ever forget that for the rest of their lives.

"So," continued Mr. Tanner, "I have thought about this Mexican Road Race. It is a spectacular race. It attracts, I am informed, cars and drivers from all over the world. It draws cars of every design from the Detroit family car to the most unusual. It is in the unusual, obviously, that I am interested. And that brings us immediately to your car—this . . . er . . . Black Tiger.

"To come to the point. I have a proposition to make to you. It is this. You will enter the Black Tiger in the Mexican Road Race. You will use oil supplied by my company. I will underwrite all the expenses connected with the race and preparations for it other than the cost of car parts and so on, which your own factory must supply.

"At the end of the race, if you are among the top three, you turn the car over to me. I pay you for the car naturally and a further twenty thousand dollars to your company in return for the right to make microphotographs of all the moving parts before and after the race, to show what wear they suffered while using my company's oil.

"These photographs, side by side with those which we are obtaining from the Bentley, will make a complete advertising campaign for me. What do you say?"

Woody turned to Rocky. It wasn't really his place to reply.

"What happens if the Black Tiger doesn't come in among the first three?" Rocky asked.

"Nothing," said Mr. Tanner. "I'll forget about the whole thing. I want a spectacular car in a spectacular race, using my oil and among the first three to finish, or the whole thing is off. I'm not interested in any degree of failure."

"Basically," said Woody, "you want us to race the Black Tiger with your oil and if we place among the top three we get twenty thousand dollars?"

"You get more than that," said Mr. Tanner. "You get nationwide publicity for the Black Tiger in every popular magazine in the United States. There will be radio and television publicity as well, of course."

Woody turned to Rocky. "I don't see how we can miss," he said, his face beaming. "From what I know of the Mexican Road Race, it's meat for the Mark II."

But Rocky was inclined to be cautious. "There are two problems to be met before we can agree to this, Mr. Tanner," she said. "The first is to get factory cooperation. I think we can get that all right. But the next may be harder. That is to get the race committee to agree to the use of your company's oil in the Mark II. In the past, as far as I know, oil and gas have been supplied by the national oil industry of Mexico. They want the publicity, too. And we may have difficulty there."

"Well, that is something you must look into," said Mr. Tanner. "Call upon me if you think I can help. I will do all I can through my various contacts."

That concluded the conversation. Mr. Tanner's chauffeur drove them back to Hermosa Beach. They were both elated at the dazzling prospect of racing the Black Tiger in the Mexican event and all that it could mean for sales of the car.

"The orders will come pouring in," Woody enthused. "Never mind about the twenty thousand dollars. There's that much in prize money anyway. But think of the reputation the Black Tiger will have if we win. The demand will be terrific."

"I'm sure the factory will agree to supply the parts," said Rocky. "Even if they are blind to the publicity value, Babs and I have enough pull to get that done. I'm just worried about using Mr. Tanner's oil. The Mexican oil people might not like that at all."

But Woody had caught fire and there was no quenching his enthusiasm now. "We'll convince them somehow," he said. "We can point to the unorthodox design of the engine. The Mercedes team were able to get special gas with a higher octane rating in one of the races by pointing out that the engines wouldn't run efficiently on what was supplied. We'll find a way, never you mind."

Already he could see himself behind the Black Tiger's wheel flashing across the Mexican deserts and around winding mountain roads. His mind was buzzing with excitement and plans.

The Mexican Road Race was the world's greatest race. There was nothing to touch it anywhere else on earth. He had long dreamed of driving in it. Now here was his chance, supplied unexpectedly by an eccentric oil millionaire. And he would drive a car far in advance of anything that had been entered in the race before.

12

THINGS BEGAN happening fast now to Woody, Rocky, and Worm. The next three weeks were full of excitement but not all of it was pleasant.

To begin with, Woody found himself on the following day in the doghouse again with Mary Jane. He called on her that evening to give her the good news and found her so cool that he sensed he was allowed in the house only as a matter of courtesy.

"What's the matter?" he asked as soon as he had a moment alone with her. "You call me up and say that you're sorry about our quarrel and ask me around. And then you treat me as if you were still mad."

"You know perfectly well what's the matter," said Mary Jane. "You told me you were going to see Mr. Tanner by yourself. And then I see you in the car with Rocky. Every time I turn around I see you with that Rocky person. Why did you lie to me?"

Woody was so angry at Mary Jane's suspicions that he very nearly walked out without an answer. But he controlled himself, and after explaining the situation Mary Jane was somewhat mollified.

"Look here," said Woody, determined to have the matter out, "you're just going to have to get used to the idea that I'm going to be around Rocky quite a bit. I'm driving her car to start with, and darned lucky to be allowed to do it, as I've said before.

"She's interested in racing and so am I, and you're not. And I'm not going to give up racing for you or anybody else. We might as well have that clear here and now."

"It's just as I said," said Mary Jane, "you care more for racing than you do for me."

"If you want to make a comparison of it—then, yes, I do. But your father's business is insurance, isn't it? And he likes it and works at it a lot of the time. But I'll bet your mother never makes any comparisons about his interest in insurance and his interest in her. The two are different things. It's the same with my father and mother. He sells real estate. But I've never heard Mom say that he loves real estate more than he loves her."

Curiously enough Mary Jane had taken this point up with her mother and her mother had said much the same thing. "Mary Jane," she had said, "a man lives in a man's world with a man's interests and has to. Woody's world is automobiles, and racing cars are part of that world. If you can't enter it with him, don't demand that he desert it for you. No man would."

These words came back to Mary Jane now. And she remembered something else her mother had said. "If you're wise, you'll try, without making a nuisance of yourself, to enter into Woody's world. Otherwise he may very easily find some girl who does. And you can't blame him if he becomes more interested in her than he is in you."

This, Mary Jane realized, was precisely the point she had reached now. She could either throw Woody and Rocky together, or she could compete with Rocky for Woody. She surrendered. "I'm sorry, Woody," she said. "I've been blue and depressed and worried about you. Forgive me?"

"Sure, honey," said Woody, and kissed her.

They spent the rest of the evening talking about the eccentric Mr. Tanner, the wonderful prospect of racing the Black Tiger in the Mexican Road Race, and all the plans which had to be made beforehand. Mary Jane felt hurt that Rocky would be going to Mexico with Woody while she wouldn't. But she said nothing.

"You said I had done nothing about getting the money together for a house payment and for furniture," said Woody. "Well, if I win this race, I'll have plenty for both."

"But the twenty thousand dollars Mr. Tanner is putting up will go to the Black Tiger people, won't it?" Mary Jane asked.

"Sure," said Woody. "But there's about the same amount or more put up for prizes by various organizations in Mexico. That would be mine and Worm's—if we win. And besides, if I pull this off I'm a cinch to get a good job with the Black Tiger people. The United States sales agency is nothing now—just Rocky and Babs doing their best. But if we do well at all in this Mexican race, they're bound to expand over here. There'll be literally scores of orders for the cars. And I'm sure Rocky will want Worm and me in as partners in the sales end of the business."

"Will Worm be your co-driver in this race?"

"I guess so," said Woody. "It won't be Rocky because the co-driver has to be a top-flight mechanic in case of trouble. And Worm is the only one who answers that description."

Mary Jane was happy. The two parted on the best terms they had enjoyed for several months. Mary Jane asked for her engagement ring back, and when Woody left the house, he felt as though he had been relieved of carrying a great weight. He really loved Mary Jane. And he believed that at last she was beginning to see the light about sports-car racing.

Of the three—Rocky, Woody, and Worm—the latter was the least excited over Mr. Tanner's plans to enter the Mark II in the Mexican Road Race. Woody gave him all the details the following day, with Rocky filling in where there was need, and his only immediate comment was that Mr. Tanner was as daft as Mrs. MacInness' cat. Mrs. MacInness' cat had apparently set a high level mark for insanity in Aberdeen, where it was known to have taken a swim in the river every day despite the traditional aversion of cats for water.

Woody agreed that maybe Mr. Tanner was as daft as Mrs. MacInness' cat, but he nevertheless meant what he said, and there was a strong streak of reason in all his insanity.

"Why doesn't he supply oil to every car in the race free?" asked Worm. "That way he'd be sure that the winning car used his oil. Why just pick the Mark II? It doesn't make any sense."

"Why worry about his reason?" asked Woody. "So

long as he picked the Mark II, that's all we're concerned with."

"Still sounds crazy to me," said Worm who, because of the beating Mr. Tanner had given the Bentley, could not get up any degree of trust for the man.

"I think I know the reason," said Rocky. "He's pretty cunning. If he wanted to supply oil to every car in the race, the Mexican oil interests might object. After all, it is a Mexican race. But if it's only one car, and we can stress that it's an unorthodox engine design, then the Mexican oil people might not mind."

Mr. Tanner's photographer meanwhile had taken all the pictures possible with his regular camera and had now arranged for parts of the Bentley to be taken to his studio for microphotographs which would dramatically show the engine wear. Since the agreement with Mr. Tanner called for microphotographs of the moving parts of the Mark II, before and after the race, its engine was also stripped down, so the photographer could take his pictures. Worm didn't like this a bit. But it wasn't his car, and he had to give way.

Meanwhile there were a dozen big items to be attended to to get ready for the Mexican Road Race. Babs and Rocky composed a long letter to the Black Tiger Company in Milan, Italy, reporting on the success of the car to date and outlining Tanner's proposition. Factory cooperation would be required, the letter said, only in the supplying of a list of spare parts which Worm drew up. These included fuel-injection pump, connecting rods, crankshaft, two complete sets of crankshaft bearings, clutch assembly, and twelve additional wheels mounted with tires. These were the principal items. There were many others including brake drums and linings, so that the list resembled an order for sufficient materials to build a new car. Rocky totaled up the price of the various items and it came to well over four thousand dollars.

Her letter stated it was intended that Woody Hartford and Worm would be driver and co-driver, and that two top-class mechanics would be found to service the car as pit crew during the race. Woody and Worm's driving records were given as a matter of course. Worm's record, when he was finally persuaded to put it down on paper, read like a calendar of every classic road race in Europe. He had not raced in the United States, but his record was ahead of many top drivers in the country.

The letter was air-mailed, and then came the task of getting entry forms and sets of rules for the Mexican Road Race, officially known as the Carrera Panamericana, through the Mexican consulate and the Asociación Nacional Automovilística (Mexico's AAA).

The Mexican Road Race, Woody knew, had a short but astounding history. To begin with, it was the world's longest road race, for the distance from the starting line at Tuxtla Gutiérrez, near the Guatemala border, to Juárez, on the United States border, was close to two thousand miles.

Unlike many of the classic races of Europe, such as the Le Mans, where drivers circled a six-mile track for twenty-four hours, no driver in the Mexican Road Race could ever be quite sure what lay ahead of him. Each mile was a new mile, not traveled before. Each corner posed the problem of how acute the angle, how much camber to help a car around, and what the road surface. Much of the route lay through mountain ranges at heights up to ten thousand feet. The road snaked around the mountains in hairpins and S-bends with precipices of several hundred feet right beside the road. A skid at the wrong moment, then, meant death.

Again the weather changed from the hot, sultry air of sea level to the cold, rarefied air of the mountaintops. And blinding sunshine could be replaced by blinding rain, and calm days by ones when the desert dusts were sent swirling like a cloud across the land by winds of thirty and forty miles an hour.

Woody read everything he could about the Mexican Road Race, and, as he read, his respect for the race mounted. It was a race for supermen, and a race for super cars.

The race was run in five laps, averaging four hundred miles each, although the mountain laps were shorter than those over the deserts and flats. One lap was run each day, and one of the greatest problems was that of servicing the cars. The rule allowed pit crews three hours to work over engines at the end of each lap and the rules were rigidly enforced. One minute over the three hours and a car was disqualified. Pit crews, therefore, had to cover each lap ahead of the cars to be on the spot when their drivers wheeled in at the end of the day's run. And that called for a great deal of organization.

Whom should they contact to work as their pit crew? What kind of transportation could they provide for them? They'd need a truck to carry all the spare parts for the Mark II. But it would have to be a truck with some kind of sleeping and living facilities for the pit crew. Woody had thought that expenses of the race would be in the neighborhood of two thousand dollars, but he could see it would be closer to six thousand now, with a truck having a special body to be obtained just for this one race. Woody comforted himself with the thought that Mr. Tanner would foot the bill.

The problem was mechanics. Whom could they obtain? Who could be trusted to work on the unorthodox engine of the Mark II?

"There's not many men I know who were brought up on Davie's *Principles and Problems of Internal Combustion Engines,*" Worm said sadly. "I wouldna trust a mon who had not read Davie."

Woody groaned. He hadn't the same faith as Worm in the renowned Davie.

"Maybe we could get a top-flight Porsche mechanic," he said. "They're rear-opposed engines similar to the Mark II. Kurt Kreuger used to be a Porsche agent. Maybe he'd know somebody."

Worm grunted. "Ye can try," he said, and added unfairly, "People who call themselves mechanics these days are little better than boilersmiths. It's not like the old days when a lad had tae serve a five-year apprenticeship. That kind's hardly to be found any more."

Woody contacted Kurt. But Kurt said he knew of no one and that he was entering the Mexican Road Race himself. So was Dave Kingston. And so was Mathews, the driver who had protested Woody's win in the Mark II.

In the end Worm said they'd have to do their own mechanical work. "We'll be as tired as dogs, nae doot," he said. "But better a tired good mechanic than a fresh bad mechanic."

That left only the problem of finding a suitable truck and getting someone who could be relied on to drive it. The latter problem was readily settled. Rocky would drive the truck with the spare parts. The finding of the truck itself was a more difficult problem. It would have to combine both a small mechanics shop and a storeroom.

Woody finally located one—an emergency truck used by the Los Angeles Rapid Transit Company for repairs to buses on highways. The truck had become outmoded as far as the transit company was concerned, but it would serve Woody's purposes excellently. The trouble was that the transit company wanted to sell it, not rent it. In this emergency Woody finally called Mr. Tanner.

"Buy it," said Mr. Tanner. "How much is wanted and to whom do I send the check?"

Woody gave him the details and a couple of days later picked up the truck and drove it into Worm's garage.

From that point on things happened fast. Official entry forms arrived, were filled in, and their acceptance acknowledged. The race officials, in reply to the inquiry about oil, proved remarkably cooperative. Cars might use whatever brand of lubricating oil they wished. It was specified, however, that the gasoline must be of Mexican origin, but octane ratings equivalent to those in the United States would be available.

All that remained was to receive a letter from the factory in Italy about the supply of parts, then they could all take off with the Black Tiger and the service truck for Mexico. The race was to start November eighteenth. Woody and Worm were anxious to have three weeks in Mexico to go over the race route and map it as carefully as they could. Rocky could bring the truck down with the tools and parts to meet with them in Mexico City a week before the start.

Worm and Woody worked in the garage late each night overhauling, tuning, and magnafluxing the Black Tiger's engine, and this work went forward without a hitch. But still there was no letter from the factory in Italy. And for the first time Woody began to have some doubts about what they might reply.

13 THE LETTER from Italy arrived just when Woody and Worm had decided to go to Mexico with the Black Tiger without it. Rocky brought it over to Woody and her face showed that something was the matter.

"What's up?" asked Woody. "Surely they're going to send the parts? They must know that this is a real big deal for them."

"They're sending the parts all right," said Rocky. "They're coming by air express and should be here in a couple of days. But there's something else. Here, you read it."

Woody took the letter from her and started reading. The first two paragraphs said that the board had met on the question of entering the Mark II in the Mexican Road Race and all were enthusiastic and wished to give their fullest support to insure the car's success. Parts were being sent by air express, despite the expense, to insure their arrival in plenty of time. Two full kits of factory tools for the Mark II were also being sent. This was what Woody had anticipated, and he didn't understand Rocky's concern. He found the reason for it in the third paragraph.

It read: "The board has the fullest confidence in the

performance of the Mark II and is anxious to do anything further it can to insure a good result in the coming race. The board realizes, however, that much will depend upon the two drivers, and accordingly has conducted its own investigations into the two gentlemen suggested, Mr. W. O. R. McNess and Mr. Woodville Hartford.

"The board, as a result of these investigations, has complete confidence in Mr. McNess. But it appears to the board that Mr. Hartford is somewhat young and inexperienced for a race calling for such skill and endurance. While his racing record is clean, the board has learned that he has twice been investigated by officials of the Southern California Sports Car Association.

"The board knows that Mr. Hartford came out of these investigations with an unblemished record. Yet with so much at stake, it is felt that a more experienced driver in whom complete confidence can be placed should be selected.

"Accordingly the board has engaged the services of Mr. Tomas Flitarri as senior driver of the Mark II in the Mexican Road Race. Mr. Flitarri will leave by a plane arriving in California October 26. Mr. Flitarri is of course known to you as one of the greatest of the European racing drivers, and we are confident that you will give him every support and facility for the coming race. . . ."

Woody read only that far and then looked at Rocky utterly dazed. The blow was the heaviest he had ever received and his mind was utterly numbed by it.

"What's the matter?" asked Worm.

"They don't want me to drive," said Woody. "They're sending out a guy by the name of Flitarri to drive the Mark II with you."

"Give me that," said Worm, and snatched the letter away. "What right have they to pick a driver?" he demanded of Rocky. "There's none better than young Woody here. Either he drives with me as co-driver or they can count me out."

Woody had by now recovered a little from the shock. "It was those darned investigations," he said partly to himself, but speaking aloud. "If it hadn't been for them the factory would have raised no objections."

"I should have settled wi' yon Mathews wi' a wrench," said Worm. "He's still talking, and his talk has got back to those people in Italy. Well, they can count Mr. Flitarri in and they can count me out. They'd better send over another Italian driver. It's Woody or nothing as far as I'm concerned."

"No," said Woody slowly, "don't say that. You've got to think of the car. This is the Mark II's big chance. If you back out, the car doesn't race. There isn't time for them to send over another driver. And if the car doesn't race, the people who lose out in the end are Rocky and Babs."

Rocky didn't say anything. Her face was white and she looked close to tears.

"Who is this guy Flitarri?" asked Woody after a silence.

"He's a top driver all right," said Worm grudgingly.

"He drove the winning car in the Le Mans and the Mille Miglia in Italy last year. He drove for the Ferrari team. They don't come any better."

"Well," said Woody, "we'd better get his name entered. At least I can be on the pit crew," he added, brightening a little. Worm gave him a pat on the shoulder and went out of the office in which they had been conferring, muttering something in Gaelic which might well have been profane.

"Woody Hartford," said Rocky, "they don't make better men than you." And she left, too.

The following day there was a cable from Italy. It said that Mr. Flitarri had been delayed and would not be arriving now until the twelfth of November. He would fly directly to Mexico City. The cable requested that they meet him there on that date with the car, and in the meantime that all the necessary pre-race arrangements be made, to be subject to his approval.

Worm didn't like the tone of this cable at all, and made no bones about it. "Subject tae his approval?" he repeated scornfully. "Well, whether he likes them or not any arrangements we make are going to stay that way. And I'm the man that will tell him so. 'Twill be a dark day when the Highland Scots start taking orders from the Italians."

Woody laughed aloud at this nationalistic remark, and Worm stared hard at him, still angry and then laughed, too. "Ah weel," he said, "if you can get a smile out of it, why should I complain?"

It was agreed that Worm and Woody would take the

Mark II down to Mexico and survey the course. A survey of the whole road, from border to border, with landmarks warning of bad corners, road intersections, bridges, and other hazards was absolutely necessary to winning the race. Meanwhile, Rocky would get the parts when they arrived and drive with them in the truck to Mexico City where they would all meet. Babs would accompany her and relieve her with the driving.

And then another passenger for the truck was added. After her talk with Woody, in which she decided to change her attitude toward racing, Mary Jane had still been very much on the side lines. She knew nothing of cars, of course, and could be of no help with the race preparations, but she longed desperately to accompany Woody and Worm to Mexico.

At last she got up her courage and went to see Rocky. The two girls knew each other, but there was nothing that could be called friendship between them, so Mary Jane was unsure of her reception, and inclined to be on the defensive. The two met for lunch in the Hermosa Beach Café without Woody's knowledge.

When they had ordered and exchanged a few pleasantries Rocky said, "That was bad news for Woody, not being able to race the Black Tiger."

"Yes," said Mary Jane.

"Tell me," said Rocky, "you were relieved really, weren't you?"

"I was," said Mary Jane. "I don't know much about this race, but the last time it was run there were several people killed, weren't there?"

Rocky nodded. "Yes," she replied, "some of the drivers and a number of spectators. It's almost impossible to control crowds along a course nearly two thousand miles long. One driver was killed trying to avoid a woman and her child who crossed the road in front of him. He deliberately drove off the road over a cliff to avoid hitting them."

"I don't understand it," said Mary Jane. "Why do they hold races like that when a number of people are killed every year?"

"Well, the public just hears about the number of people who are killed," said Rocky. "Everybody in the road-racing business wishes it were possible to hold a road race without a single accident or fatality. But the lives of a lot of people are saved by road racing.

"Take brakes. Automobile engines have been getting more and more powerful. Two hundred horsepower is normal in a family car these days. Are brakes adequate for cars with such powerful engines? In one of the earlier Mexican Road Races, almost every car suffered from fading brakes. Engineers went to work to devise better brakes, brakes that would operate under grueling conditions, when brake drums have been heated to enormous temperatures. Now the improved brakes are on every family car.

"Then there's the problem of the stability of a car. When a car turns over, it's not always the result of fast driving. Sometimes it's just that too much cushioning and springing have been incorporated. The car sways heavily on a corner, and the driver loses control and it goes over.

"Road racing isn't a blood sport. It's dangerous and

always will be dangerous. But it had its uses in insuring the safety of millions of drivers and their families who never intend to race a car in all their lives."

"Well," said Mary Jane, "you asked me, and that's how I feel. I'm glad Woody's not driving."

There was a pause for a while.

"Rocky," said Mary Jane, "I know that Woody will never lose his interest in sports cars. And I was silly to try to stop him. But I don't want to be left on the outside. Do you think I could go to Mexico with you? I want to see the race with Woody, that is if I wouldn't be in the way." Her voice was very humble, and Rocky felt suddenly friendly toward Mary Jane.

"Of course you can come," she said. "There'll be plenty of room in the truck. And you can spell Babs and me at driving. That will make it easier for us all."

"Gosh," said Mary Jane, elated, "I could fix coffee and sandwiches and stuff like that."

"Why didn't you ask Woody about it?" Rocky questioned.

"Well, I didn't want to interfere with him, or have him think I was pushing my way in. That's one reason. And then because the Black Tiger is your car, it seemed right that I should ask you."

Rocky considered Mary Jane's new attitude and Woody's acceptance of the fact that he couldn't drive the Black Tiger. "You know," she said, "people are growing up very fast around here."

14

BY THE beginning of November, Woody and Worm with the Mark II were in the tropical city of Tuxtla Gutiérrez, near the southern border of Mexico. They had driven down from Hermosa Beach, a grueling journey of nine days, and now were ready to start a survey of the route of the Mexican Road Race, to start in two weeks' time.

For this survey Worm had collected some strange equipment. He had a pot of orange paint, another of red, and a third of bright blue. He also had a number of pieces of two-by-four lumber, a heavy mallet, and several bags of nails, some planks of white pine, and a dozen yards of cheap cloth of different colors. The luggage compartment of the Mark II, where the engine was located on conventional automobiles, was full of this strange collection, and several assorted pieces of lumber stuck up around the driver's and co-driver's seats.

"Cripes, what are you getting all that junk for?" Woody asked. Most of the material arrived the day they were to start their survey.

"Tae mark the route with," said Worm. "Did ye think I was going to build a house?"

"You mean you're going to leave a trail of red, blue,

and orange paint from here to the United States?" Woody demanded.

"I am if need be," said Worm with great determination. "Didna ye notice that there were very few signs along the road warning of intersections, bridges, and so on?"

Woody had thought it was only necessary to make his own map of the road and had brought a big sketch pad with which to do this. His plan was that keying the map to the mileage recorded on the speedometer he would be able to locate dangerous corners, blind intersections, and bridges before they were reached. All the co-driver would then have to do would be to warn the driver of a particular intersection or corner or bridge coming up by reference to the sketches.

"Make yere sketches anyway," Worm said. "They'll be useful, without a doubt. But we'll need markers, too."

So they set out, and as they did so all their worst fears of the route were confirmed. The first leg of the race would be from Tuxtla Gutiérrez to Oaxaca. It climbed all the way up into the Sierra Madre range, the road snaking around hairpins, switchbacks, and loops, through cuttings, and over bridges where the earth fell away into wild gorges.

Worm drove. It was the first time Woody had seen him do anything like race driving, and Woody was impressed. He changed gears in a fraction a second, with an efficient jab of his arm on the gearshift. He was somewhat faster than Woody in slipping from fourth down to second. He didn't go into third but made the change direct and never missed it once.

At their first stop Woody asked him about this. "I'd hate to risk doing that myself," he said. "I'd be afraid of ripping out the whole gearbox."

"It's no' something tae be done casually," said Worm. "Ye have tae know the gear ratios and watch the tachometer closely. If ye know the ratios of the gears, ye can tell by watching the tach and listening tae the engine whether it's safe tae change from fourth tae second. I tried it once on a Bugatti in a tight spot from fourth tae first."

"What happened?" asked Woody.

"Too many rpms. I swallowed a valve and wrecked the gearbox."

Twelve miles out of Tuxtla, Worm met with the first hazard of the course he wanted to mark. The road plunged upward to the crown of a hill, dropped swiftly, and still going down turned in a tight hairpin. Worm took the Mark II back over the hill and shot this hazard several times. Then he got out and looked around. There was a small lone scrub pine growing by the side of the road. He dug out his pot of red paint and a brush and solemnly painted the trunk of the tree red.

"Make a note o' that," he said to Woody. " 'Red tree trunk shut off and change doon tae second.' " Woody began to see that Worm's method of marking the course was eminently practical. He noted the mileage from Tuxtla to this particular spot as an extra guide.

Worm had a code already worked out for danger spots. He used red for bad hairpins, blue for bridges hidden around a bend, orange for sudden dips or other turns not so bad as the hairpins but still calling for a change of speed.

By the time they got to Oaxaca, marking the end of the first lap, they had used up a pot of red paint and a pot of blue. Sometimes there was no natural object which could be painted to warn of a hazard ahead. Here the pieces of two-by-fours and the planks came into use. Worm made his own signposts out of them and painted them the appropriate color. Woody made a note of which side of the road all these signs were on and their distance from Tuxtla. He also made a sketch of the kind of hazard which lay ahead.

The road surface on this first leg, apart from the innumerable twists and turns of the road itself, provided a danger of its own. It was a good firm roadbed but surfaced with sharp gravel. There were a number of places where it had washed out and been repaired. But the repaired surface had sunk slightly under the weight of the traffic. Hitting one of these slight depressions at more than a hundred miles an hour would be sufficient to throw a car out of control. But there was no way of marking all such spots. They had to be content with marking the worst hazards. The rest had to be left to the observation of the driver and good luck.

At Oaxaca they examined the tires on the Mark II. There had been plenty of tread on them when they left Tuxtla. Now they were worn almost smooth. One of the rear tires was worn nearly down to the canvas. Worm shook his head solemnly.

"Mon," he said, "that's where most of the trouble is

likely tae be. We'll have tae change all four tires at the end of the first lap, and we'll be lucky if we get through the lap without having tae use some spares."

Woody inspected the brake drums and found them too hot to touch, yet Worm had not been driving at racing speeds and so had not had to do the kind of braking for corners that would be necessary during the race. "I think the major trouble is going to be with the brakes," he said. "You'll be lucky if they don't fade on you. Brother, those are hot."

"If I was doing the driving," said Worm, "I wouldn't press it through those mountains. It's a long race. The time tae speed up is on the flat after Mexico City."

That evening they bought a new set of tires for the Mark II in Oaxaca. There would be plenty for the race when Rocky arrived with the service truck, but Worm didn't want to touch the Italian Pirelli racing spares that the Black Tiger carried. They had no difficulty getting tires, for in anticipation of a demand with the road race coming, local garages had laid in a stock of every size.

The second day the two continued their survey, and found the leg from Oaxaca to Mexico City even tougher than the first. The road surface was better, being of asphalt or concrete. But this road swooped and rose and dived over the shoulders of mountains, around blind corners, and across gorges and ravines—a beautiful highway plunging through a maze of geography, climbing relentlessly upward until a peak was reached around the city of Puebla. The road went through the city with many twists and turns, and Worm wondered what the situation would be in this city when the race was on.

Then several score cars, going full blast, would thunder through the crowds packed on either side and the police would have a mammoth job preventing injury to spectators.

On this leg Worm did some more of his "landscape painting," as he called it, coating available tree trunks and rocks with bright blue, red, and orange paint, as markers for the hazards ahead. Woody made a sketch of the particular hazard and noted the mileage from Oaxaca of each. By the end of the leg in Mexico City the Mark II's brakes had faded almost completely because of constant use through the mountains.

Worm was worried. "I've not been driving at racing speeds," he said. "If the brakes went out that much on a practice run, there'd be no brakes left during the race. I'd hate tae have the brakes fade completely back there on those mountain bends. A mon would learn tae play the harp in one lesson if something like that happened."

"We'll have to work out some method of cooling the brake drums," said Woody.

"Aye," said Worm. "Cooling would help. But the main thing is not to use the brakes except when absolutely necessary."

That night they inspected the brakes. The drums, which were of the new alloy, had held up well enough, but the linings were down to the rivets and as slick as oil stones.

The Mark II engine, clutch, transmission, and rear end had held up magnificently through the mountain trials. Worm had not a word of complaint about any of these departments. But he noted that the clutch housing was hot—very hot, and was worried about the clutch burning out under the strain of all-out mountain climbing.

From Mexico City, which lies at an altitude of seven thousand five hundred feet, the road came down from the mountains and then leveled off across the great central plateau of Mexico. Here the hazards were much fewer and this, as Worm had said, was the place to make up for lost time in the mountains. He was determined to advise the Italian driver, Flitarri, not to press the Mark II in the mountains. The best that could be hoped for on such a tortuous route was four or five miles an hour faster than the other cars in the race. But that narrow advantage would be paid for in tremendous engine strain, tire and brake wear, and greatly increased danger.

On the flat after Mexico City, which would be the third leg of the race, speed could be increased. That was the time to let the Mark II go full bore, for there were few hazards from Mexico City to the finish line at Ciudad Juárez.

The two relined the brakes in Mexico City and went on to León, which marked the end of the third lap. They found the road excellent, fairly level, with few dangerous corners or sudden dips which had to be marked. Then they came back to Mexico City. They had to find a garage in which to retune the Mark II, install a ten-gallon auxiliary gas tank, and work out some method of cooling the brake drums and clutch.

Worm spent a whole day searching Mexico City for a

suitable garage. The trouble was not that Mexico City, a completely modern metropolis, lacked garages, but that Worm was not easily satisfied with the garages he inspected.

His method was to park the Mark II out of sight and stroll into a garage and look the place over. He was not impressed by white-coated foremen, by glittering showrooms, by pneumatic jacks, and wall charts showing a cross-section through a variety of automobile engines. That, he explained to Woody, was just for show.

In all the garages into which he went he managed to get into conversation with some of the working mechanics, and without them being aware of it, looked over their tools.

He shook his head over them all. The mechanics' toolkits didn't come up to Worm's standards and he would not be shaken from the view that a good mechanic lavishes as much care on his tools as a good violinist gives to his violin. He spotted wrenches with strained jaws, screw drivers with rounded ends, pliers with damaged cutters, and came away.

Woody began to get disgusted. He could not accompany Worm on these tours of inspection for he had to remain with the Mark II. "Look," he said, "we can go on like this for a week. You'll find tools in the same condition in every garage in the United States."

"Aye," said Worm, "but not my garage. And it's one like mine that I'm looking for—a wee place wi' a real mechanic in it."

They came at last to an unpretentious garage on the

northern outskirts of the city. It boasted only two fuel pumps, had a single hoist, and its walls were of corrugated iron.

"I'm coming with you," said Woody. "I'm sick of sitting in the car with people asking me questions in Spanish when I can't understand a word they say. What does *parabrisa* mean, anyway?"

"Windshield," said Worm unexpectedly.

"When did you learn to speak Spanish?" Woody demanded.

"I don't speak Spanish," said Worm, "but I had brains enough tae learn the Spanish words for a few automobile parts when I knew we were coming here."

By this time they were in the garage and the proprietor came forward to greet them and ask their business. Worm, using English, sign language, and a few Spanish words, said he would like to look over the shop. The proprietor was a small, huskily-built man dressed in coveralls. His beard was so heavy that although clean shaven his chin looked blue. It occurred to Woody that he resembled a stunted giant—heavily-muscled but only five foot six.

"Certainly," said the man, in English. "Allow me to take you around. It is only a small place, but it is mine and we do good work here." He showed them the workbench, single hydraulic lift, and his tools. They were all carefully arranged in a series of homemade drawers. Everything was in its place, and the shop was fully, though not elaborately, equipped with a small lathe, buffer, drill, and other power tools.

"Have ye been long working as an automobile mechanic?" asked Worm.

"About fifteen years, Señor," the Mexican, whose name was Perez, replied. "As a boy I was very interested and learned all I could. Most of what I learned I got from books. We Mexicans are not supposed to be a mechanical people. Actually we are just as mechanically minded as anyone else, though we haven't got the same facilities. One can learn a great deal from books." He opened a drawer and put a greasy, well-thumbed volume on the workbench.

"This was my greatest teacher," he concluded.

The original cover of the volume had long been gone, so the book was now bound between two pieces of heavy canvas. Worm opened the makeshift canvas cover.

"Davie's *Principles and Problems of Internal Combustion Engines*," he cried. "Mon, ye're just the mechanic I've been looking for." He seized the surprised Perez by the hand and shook it vigorously.

"Let me see that," said Woody, and picked up the volume. It was in Spanish and he could not read a line of it, but there were the familiar diagrams and formulae he had glanced at so many times in Worm's copy. "Well, I'll be hanged," he said. "How many languages is that Davie book published in?"

"I wouldna be surprised if we found a copy of it in Lhasa, Tibet," said Worm. "Away wi' ye and fetch the Black Tiger and be sharp about it."

The car had been parked around a corner and was, as usual, the center of a crowd of spectators. Woody had to shoo them off, and when he drove around to Perez's garage, the crowd followed him. They were shouting and laughing and gesticulating, and flowed into the garage so that Woody could hardly get out of the car. Perez took command of the situation. He made an address which was so impassioned it sounded to Woody like an invitation to overthrow the government by armed force. But the crowd withdrew to a respectful distance.

Worm went round to the rear of the Mark II and opened the hood. There was a gasp of awe from the spectators. But their surprise was as nothing to the look on Perez's face. He seemed to be in the presence of a shrine. His lips moved with unspoken emotion and his eyes gleamed.

"Señor Worm," he said at last, "I wonder if you know what a great honor it is for me to have such an automobile in my garage. I have repaired hundreds of cars. Two years ago I was privileged to have here, on the spot where you now stand, a Rolls-Royce belonging to a very wealthy Englishman. The car had become sick in the carburetors and it was I, Manuel Jesús Gonsalves y Perez, who cured the illness. But such a car as this I have never seen before. Would the señor do me a great favor?"

"Sure," said Worm.

"Would the señor and his friend stand beside the car here in my garage so I can take a photograph of it on my premises?"

"Sure," said Worm again.

Perez bustled off and returned with an old-fashioned folding Kodak camera. He backed off to get his garage name in the picture. The Mark II was wheeled out in front and then Perez shot his picture with the help of all kinds of advice about the artistic arrangement of the car from the spectators.

When he had finished, he asked whether the car was to be raced in the Carrera Panamericana—the Mexican Road Race, and Worm replied that it was.

This was too much for Perez to keep to himself. He went before the crowd and addressed them again, pointing to the car and repeating the phrase "Carrera Panamericana." There were loud cheers and cries of *"bueno"* and *"bravo."*

"Señor," said Perez, "every year I close my shop and follow the Panamericana. I know every driver and co-driver who has been in the race by name, but have never met any of them. Never has one of the cars been in my garage. They go naturally to the big garages in the city and have their own crews work on them. Whatever I may do to help you, Señor, I will do. This car, the Black Tiger, Mark II, is mine now. I adopt it. I give it my love and my skill. I will not charge you a penny for time or materials. Just let me work on it, Señor, with you and you will make me a happy and proud man."

Woody had never heard such emotion expressed over an automobile. He loved cars in his own way; they were indeed his life, but the attitude of Perez was almost one of adoration.

Worm was touched. The warmth and sincerity of the Mexican mechanic appealed to the Highland Scot in him, for the Scottish Highlanders are by no means an unemotional people. "Mon," he said, "if ye were trained on Davie and ye love the car, that's good enough for me. Count yourself in."

He didn't say so at the time, but he congratulated himself secretly on not only having found a top-rate mechanic, but also a potential member of the Mark II's pit crew for the coming race.

15 WITH THE aid of Perez, who proved an excellent mechanic, the Mark II was tuned for the race. Actually the car was far more than tuned. It was inspected in as complete detail as possible without stripping the engine. The brakes were again lined and the lines along which the brake fluid flowed inspected inch by inch. Special attention was given to the master cylinder to be absolutely sure there was no leakage of fluid. The whole ignition was checked over, fuel-injection system cleaned and adjusted, tappets set, and the clutch taken out, inspected for wear, and reassembled.

In all this work Perez took part with a kind of devotion. He was utterly tireless and completely willing to perform even the most menial chore. He became exasperated only when he had to leave the Mark II to gas up a car calling at his garage, and eventually, to save himself this kind of interruption, he hung signs on his gas pumps announcing in Spanish that he was out of gas.

This struck Worm's thrifty soul as carrying matters too far. He argued with Perez that he shouldn't turn down customers to work on the Mark II. But Perez replied simply, "Señor Worm, such interruptions as that and I might do something wrong. Then you would lose the race and every time you remembered me, you would do so with anger and feel that all the mechanics of Mexico are worthless.

"No, Señor Worm, for a few pesos I would not take such risks which might harm the reputation of my country."

Perez was very conscious and proud of his nationality. He looked upon himself not merely as a mechanic but a Mexican mechanic, and felt that the reputation of his people rested upon his own shoulders. When Worm asked him whether he would join the official pit crew of the Black Tiger, Mark II, he was delighted. He immediately had a sign made announcing that he was a member of the Black Tiger's pit crew and placed this prominently on the front of his garage. It tremendously increased his prestige in the neighborhood.

After the tuning and painstaking inspection of the Mark II there was still the problem of designing some system of cooling the brake drums and the clutch.

The rear brakes were likely to give the most trouble. They not only had the heaviest job to do because of the weight of the engine near them, which would make them heat up that much faster, but they also picked up a great deal of the engine heat.

A wall of asbestos was placed between the brake drums and the engine block to cut out that source of heat. Vents were then cut in the streamlined body of the Black Tiger so that some of the air flow past the car would be directed through the coachwork and onto the rear brake drums. Since the Black Tiger had a rear engine, clutch and flywheel were behind the driver. Worm cut away a section of the fire wall to provide freer air movement around the flywheel and clutch housing. He made ducts of wide-diameter hose to direct a stream of air onto the clutch and cut ventilating holes in the top of the clutch housing.

Then came the task of installing the auxiliary ten-gallon gas tank. This had been made in Worm's garage in Hermosa Beach but not yet installed. It was placed in the luggage compartment in front and connected to the fuel-injection system, with its own lines and pump. A switch was installed on the dashboard to cut in the auxiliary tank when needed. Worm didn't like the idea of the auxiliary tank.

"It's a lot of extra gasoline to carry and we may not need it," he said when they were making the installation.

"If your number-one tank goes dry in the middle of a leg, you'll need it real bad," replied Woody.

"We could carry two four-gallon cans in the car," said Worm.

"Not according to the rules this year, you can't," said Woody. "All gas tanks have to be properly installed and connected to the engine. No loose cans allowed."

"Well," said Worm, "it'll help distribute the weight better." But he still didn't like it.

Woody had told Perez about their survey of the road, and Perez asked, deferentially, whether he could see Woody's various sketch maps of corners and other hazards. Woody showed them to him. Perez looked them over carefully and then began making sketches of his own. It developed that he knew the road in detail, which was not surprising since he had followed every race. He was able to improve Woody's sketches and point to a few dangers that had been missed.

"Before this turn here, Señor," he said, "there is a very bad corner which we call the Corner of Death. You have not got it marked. It is twenty-five miles out of Tuxtla."

"I don't remember any bad corner at that point," said Woody.

"It is very tricky," said Perez. "The corner is absolutely safe at normal speeds, but there is a very slight incline from the inside of the corner out. It is not much more than an inch in a foot. But at ninety miles an hour, Señor, it is enough to throw you off the road. It should be marked."

"Is there any landmark near it?" asked Worm.

"Yes," said Perez. "The road at this point travels along the side of a cliff. If you glance over the cliff, you will see two burned tree stumps. When you see them, that is the time to cut off and change down."

"Two burned tree stumps?" said Worm.

"Yes," said Perez. "The stumps are about ten feet high and easy to see. They stand among a number of white rocks. The trees were burned in the last race when a car went over the cliff and caught fire. Since then this place has been known as the Corner of Death. It is very bad and few people mark it in surveying the course."

All in all, Woody concluded, they'd found a real treasure when Worm discovered Perez in his modest garage.

The next day Mary Jane, Rocky, and Babs arrived in the service truck. They were introduced to Perez and told that he and Woody would constitute the Black Tiger's pit crew. Rocky was delighted. She spoke Spanish and was soon engaged in an animated conversation with Perez who was very complimented that one of the American girls could speak his language. Ever after he showed special attention to Rocky.

Perez said he had a station wagon which was fitted out for hunting of which he was very fond. It had two bunks in it, a stove, and an icebox. He suggested that the ladies use the station wagon and he and Woody would drive the service truck during the race. One of the girls could use a sleeping bag and sleep in the front seat of the station wagon.

Worm accepted immediately and wanted to pay for the use of the station wagon. But even when he explained that all expenses were being met by Mr. Tanner, Perez would not hear of it. He seemed to have no great regard for money though he was not wealthy.

"One does not take money from friends," he said.

By now the whole of Mexico City was in a fervor over the approaching race. Worm and Woody had taken rooms at a good hotel in Mexico City the first night they were there. The girls were also registered at this hotel. Soon the whole building was filled with people connected with the race. Drivers and crews from all parts of the world checked in daily. There were entries from Germany, which had a factory-backed team of three Mercedes 300 SLR's; from Italy with three Lancias and four Maseratis and two 4.9 liter Ferraris; from England, France, Sweden, Argentina, the United States, and, of course, Mexico itself.

The newspapers were crowded daily with stories about cars and drivers. The Mark II came in for a good share of this publicity, with Perez answering the questions and beaming proudly before the reporters. But he always insisted that the photographer's limelight be focused on Woody, Worm, and Rocky. He practically had to be dragged into the pictures himself. He was tremendously proud, however, when a picture of himself appeared in a leading newspaper, identifying him as one of the pit crew of the revolutionary new car.

Indeed, the decision to add Perez to the Mark II's pit crew made Worm and Woody immensely popular with the Mexican people. Most drivers brought in mechanics from their own countries. There were twelve German mechanics to service the Mercedes SL's, and a host of somewhat excitable Italian mechanics for the Lancias and Maseratis and Ferraris. But undoubtedly the mystery car of the race was the Mark II and for her pit crew a Mexican mechanic had been chosen.

The compliment was taken as one to the Mexican people and made the Black Tiger the favorite of the race at least to the Mexicans. Woody and Worm became well-known figures and there were cries of *"Olé, el Tigre Negro!"* when they appeared in public and were spotted.

One night, as a relief from the strain and worry of race preparations, the whole party, Woody, Worm, Mary Jane, Rocky, Babs, and Perez went to a night club for dinner. They were hardly seated before the spotlight was focused on them, and the cries of *"Olé, el Tigre Negro!"* and "Viva, Señor Worm," "Viva, Señor Woody" filled the room. The band leader announced the next number would be dedicated to the "Black Tiger" and her crew. It was a pretty hot number, composed for the most part of a trumpet solo with enough fanfares for a bullfight. Woody believed it was impromptu—composed on the spot. But the number became known as the "Black Tiger Roll" and a favorite in the city overnight.

The following morning the Italian driver, Tomas Flitarri, arrived. Woody had been preparing for his arrival for a long time, trying to get his thinking straightened out so he would not dislike the man. He kept telling himself it would be much better for Rocky that Flitarri, a thoroughly seasoned driver, pilot the car and that he was too young to be driving in a race that demanded the utmost in racing experience.

But though he had often repeated these facts to himself, he still could not get over a sharp stab of disappointment when he realized that he wouldn't be behind the wheel in the big race. The Black Tiger was part of himself. He'd proven the first model. That made the car his in a way that only a racing driver could understand. And now he had to turn this car over to someone else.

He fought these thoughts back as the gleaming white four-engined plane carrying Flitarri taxied to a halt on the runway of the International Airport at Mexico City.

He and Worm had come alone to meet Flitarri and were waiting anxiously at the arrival gate. The man was easy to recognize from his photographs. He had a thin, almost Arabic face and stood a little short of six feet. He was muffled up in a long overcoat that reached below his calves and wore a soft hat of green felt.

"Mr. Flitarri?" asked Worm as he came through the gate. "I'm McNess, your co-driver in the Black Tiger."

"Ah," said Mr. Flitarri, showing a set of remarkably strong white teeth in a quick smile. "Delighted to meet you. How is the car? In good shape, I hope? You have checked it over thoroughly, no doubt. We have not much time, but I could not get away sooner. Still, Antonio will be able to give it a final inspection."

"Antonio?" asked Worm.

"Yes," said Flitarri. "He is getting the bags. My mechanic. Of course I brought him with me. I have never raced without him in my pit crew."

16 THE ARRIVAL of Flitarri with his own mechanic to serve in the pit crew very nearly wrecked the whole Black Tiger, Mark II, entry. It was a terrible blow to Woody. Already ousted from the position of driver (though his name had been retained as a driver in the car's registration papers), he now was supplanted as one of the pit crew.

But it had to be that way. The alternatives were that Flitarri, sent out by the factory, would not drive. Or that the enthusiastic and highly skilled Perez be dropped from the pit crew after having been promised a place in it.

The rules of the race said that only two men could work on any car at the end of each leg. For a third man even to touch it would automatically disqualify the car. Now there was one extra pit crew member.

Worm was for keeping Woody. Rocky, as the car's owner, wanted Woody in the pit crew, too, and insisted that Perez be dropped. Flitarri was indifferent so long as his own mechanic, Antonio, was a member of the crew. The crisis came at a meeting in Woody's hotel room at which Flitarri, Antonio (who spoke no English and didn't know what all the fuss was about), Woody, Worm, and Perez were present.

"I am not concerned so long as Antonio is in my crew. Otherwise I do not drive," said Flitarri for the tenth time.

"Ye've nae right tae bring oot yere own mechanic without notifying us," said Worm savagely. "Ye leave all the race preparations tae us and then dump something like this in our laps."

Flitarri shrugged. He felt his importance put him above these minor squabbles.

"It is perfectly all right," said Perez. "I was the last man invited. Somebody else has turned up. It is for me to give way."

Woody had been examining his hands all through the conversation as if he had only just discovered them and was keenly interested in their construction. He looked up now, his face pale.

"This race has been jinxed for me from the start," he said. "There were all those inquiries into my racing record before we got started. Then I got bumped as a driver. And now there's this pit crew situation . . ."

"Jinxed?" said Flitarri, suddenly taking an interest. "You have some special kind of a jinx that operates against you? Like a bird, huh?"

"Birds?" asked Woody.

"Birds are death to me," said Flitarri dramatically. "They are evil creatures for Flitarri. I remember to this day my first Grand Prix race at Monaco. Somebody had a canary in the pit.

" 'Take that bird out of here!' I demanded, and it was done. But too late. In the fiftieth lap, with a ten-lap lead, my oil pump went out and the engine of my Ferrari seized up. Birds! I cannot tolerate them." He lapsed into silence, brooding over the evil of birds. Woody almost forgot what had brought the topic up.

"When I am killed in a race," said Flitarri dully, "it will be because of a bird."

"I don't know about birds," said Woody. "But there's a hoodoo on this race for me. It's just not in the cards for me to take any part in it, so let's go ahead with Antonio and Perez in the pit and I'll just join the spectators."

Worm tried to argue him out of it. He was outraged at the prospect that Woody, of whom he was very fond, would have no part in the race. Perez repeated that he could not possibly replace Woody. But Woody knew deep inside that, hard as the blow was for him, it would be harder for Perez. The sturdy little Mexican mechanic was devoted to the Black Tiger and to the road race. He had often said that he felt himself the representative of his people. And in that light he could not be dropped.

"Let's quit the arguing and get down to brass tacks," said Woody. "Perez is as good if not a better mechanic than I. We've got to think of the car, not the personalities. The car's got to be given every chance. So let's settle on Antonio and Perez and leave it at that."

Finally it was agreed. Woody would step down once more. When Mary Jane heard of the decision she nearly wept. She knew very well now how much racing, especially this race, meant to Woody. There was no comfort she could offer him, but she was humbled by his enormous gallantry in always putting the car first.

"You've got a better man in Woody than you realize," said Rocky.

Mary Jane nodded. She was beginning to appreciate this herself.

Having made the decision, Woody was determined that nobody was going to make a martyr of him and there would be no long faces about it. The following day Perez reported that he was feeling very sick and did not know whether he would be up to the work ahead. Woody took him aside.

"Listen," he said, "it's real nice of you to pull a sick act right now. I appreciate it, believe me, but I'm not going to let you get away with it. So snap out of it."

"Señor Woody," said Perez, "I have a sickness of the heart."

"So've I," said Woody. "But we'll both get over it."

"It is possible that I might drop dead," said Perez, but without much conviction.

"Funny you never mentioned that before," said Woody. "Even if you had a bad sickness of the heart, I'll bet you wouldn't drop dead until the Mark II rolled over the finish line." That ended Perez' sickness, but he developed a hero-worshiping attitude toward Woody which was at times a little hard to bear.

The same day Woody ran into Kurt Kreuger and Dave Kingston. The two with their pit crews had been in Mexico for three weeks, but this was their first meeting there with Woody for they had been surveying the course and had made their headquarters at León.

Kurt was driving a Mercedes and Dave a Jag. "Sorry to hear about your bad luck," said Kurt in his slow, stolid voice.

"We could get you into one of the other pit crews if you want," said Dave.

"Thanks," said Woody, "but it's the Black Tiger for me or no other."

"I understand," said Kurt. "She's your car." He was smoking a Mexican cigar and took it from his mouth and examined it with disfavor. "Real hot driver that Flitarri," he said. "One of the best. But he sure is a temperamental guy. You heard about the canary?"

Woody nodded. Kurt looked around him slowly and said, "Wonder what would happen if a guy was to present him with a canary just before the start. You know. Just put it on the driver's seat in a cage."

"Kurt Kreuger," said Woody, "when did you start playing dirty pool?"

"I was just wondering," said Kurt mildly.

"Well, forget about it," said Woody.

The day of the start Woody, Rocky, Babs, and Mary Jane decided to stay in Oaxaca with the station wagon. With this plan they'd be there to witness the finish of the first leg. Perez and Antonio went to the starting point at Tuxtla with the service truck to make last-minute adjustments. It had been decided to install a set of lower-ratio rear-end gears for the first two legs to give the Mark II additional torque for the mountains and bends.

The start was for six in the morning with the bigger sports cars going off first at one-minute intervals. They would be followed by the Detroit production cars, then the small sports cars. The time of each car's start would be taken and the time of the finish to work out the elapsed time for the leg. Over-all elapsed times on all five legs to the border would decide the over-all winner and the various class winners.

Woody selected a spot near the finish line on the outskirts of Oaxaca and stayed there in the station wagon all night. The girls joined him the following morning.

Then they waited. They turned on the radio and listened to the broadcast of the start. The announcer first reviewed the rules, pointing out that each car had been given a safety inspection and that the distance of the first leg was three hundred and seventy-two miles. Cars in the different classes had to finish the leg in a specified time, otherwise they were disqualified. The time for the class in which the Black Tiger was running, the sports cars of two thousand ccs and over, was eight hours.

First off was the Mercedes team, next the Lancias and Maseratis, and then the Black Tiger. They could hear the roar from the crowd as the Black Tiger took its place on the elevated starting ramp so that all could see the car as it taxied up to the line. Woody's heart pounded. If matters had been different, he would be the one sitting behind the wheel and hearing the crowd shouting, *"Olé, el Tigre Negro!"* For a while he could not trust himself to speak. Then he said, "If everything goes all right they should be rolling into Oaxaca shortly after midday. They've got to be here by two o'clock or they're disqualified."

They listened to the start of the other cars and the remarks of the commentator. The broadcast was in English on one station and Spanish on the other, and the

English broadcaster really knew his stuff. Woody could picture the cars on the starting ramp with a sea of faces staring up from below. He experienced some of the sensations of the drivers as the green flag fell and they roared down the ramp with nearly four hundred miles of mountain road racing ahead of them.

He heard Dave Kingston start and Kurt Kreuger (both were private entries without factory backing) and a host of his old racing friends, and then he didn't want to hear any more. He got out of the station wagon, walked a little distance off, and lit a cigarette. His hands were trembling.

Mary Jane watched him go but didn't follow him. She sensed that this was one time to let him be alone.

After a while Woody returned, and they drank some coffee and ate some sandwiches. Woody found that he was talking all the time of the Black Tiger's prospects. And as the minutes crept by into hours, he could not keep his eyes off his watch waiting for the first cars to appear.

Two broadcast companies had sent crews out of Oaxaca to points along the road to keep listeners informed of the progress of the race, but the reception from these crews was so bad that in the end Woody turned the radio off in disgust.

"We'll just wait," he said, looking at his watch again.

Twelve o'clock came at last and there was still no sign of the first car. Then twelve-fifteen. By twelve-thirty the crowd had swarmed all over the road, blocking it completely in their anxiety to catch a glimpse of the cars which must be due at any moment now.

The police could do nothing to get the crowd back off the road. Woody's face was ashen. "When those Mercedes start streaming into that crowd at a hundred and fifty miles per hour, this place is going to look like a slaughterhouse."

Three minutes later the first Mercedes appeared. The car plummeted straight for the crowd and the crowd split to let it through. Everybody was cheering and laughing. The Mexicans seemed to regard the race as a bullfight with the car as the bull. They had very nearly blocked the road again when the second Mercedes appeared. Once more they split just enough to let it go whizzing past them. Every Mexican and Indian in the crowd seemed convinced that he could run faster than a Mercedes going full bore.

Miraculously there were no accidents. But the strain on each driver must have been terrific seeing this human ocean right in front of his car. The Mercedes came in, then the Lancias, then the Maseratis. It was like a procession, the order unchanged since the start. Unchanged, that is, except that the Black Tiger had not yet appeared.

"Something's wrong," said Rocky. "Here come the Detroit production cars." It was true. Two Lincolns swept down the road ahead, parting the human sea, to be followed by a Dodge and a Pontiac.

Then came the Black Tiger. Woody could see little of it over the heads of the crowd, but what he saw was sufficient. The windshield was smashed and Worm was driving.

"I'm going round to the garage area," said Woody,

and dashed out of the station wagon. "Something went wrong."

Woody had a pass to the garage area and arrived shortly after the Mark II rolled in. "Hi, Worm," he shouted as soon as he caught sight of the car. "What happened?"

Worm, still behind the wheel and groping for a cigarette, looked around, grinned, and said, "We got the bird."

"The bird?" repeated Woody, mystified.

Worm nodded to the smashed windshield. "Right through there," he said. "A turkey buzzard. Big, slow, clumsy thing tried to fly across the road. We hit it at a hundred and ten and Flitarri caught it right in the face. He hasn't been the same man since."

This was obviously true. Flitarri was sitting in the co-driver's seat staring ahead of him but saying nothing. The muscles of his jaw were working under the sallow skin of his face.

"Is he hurt?" Woody asked.

"Got a couple of black eyes and a headache," said Worm. "Otherwise he's not much hurt. Outside, that is. Inside he's all busted up. Lost his nerve. You know about him and birds."

Flitarri now got out of the car, slammed the door with a dramatic gesture, and shouted, "I'm through. I've had a warning. If I drive any more in this race, I'll be killed. The race is over."

The Italian's cool decision to drop out of the race was too much for Woody. All his pent-up disappointments, carefully controlled up to this point, overwhelmed him. "Listen, you big jerk," he said, "you're not going to wash out the Black Tiger just because you're scared of birds. You're going to drive that car even if you hit a whole aviary full of them."

"No," said Flitarri. "I know these omens. I have had a warning of disaster—of death. I will drive no more in this race."

Worm had by now found a cigarette, lit it, and thirstily sucked in a lungful of tobacco smoke. "That's what the gentleman says," he said calmly. "He's not driving any more. We nearly went off the road when that turkey buzzard hit. I don't know how we didn't. But when we stopped finally, he got out, and it took me several minutes and a little wrench waving to get him back in again. He wanted to stay right where he was. Swore he'd be killed if he drove another mile. So I took over, and he went into a kind of a fog."

"Where does this leave the Mark II?" demanded Woody. "He's got to drive!"

"I will not enter that car again," said Flitarri flatly. "I take the plane back to Italy tomorrow. The race is over for me."

"I'll tell you where it leaves the car," said Worm, ignoring him. "It leaves it with a new driver, namely Woody Hartford. You're still registered as one of the drivers of this little bomb. And the rules say that a driver can withdraw and be replaced by another at the end of the lap but not in the middle. All we got to do is see the stewards and get your name put down as the new driver."

It took an hour to do this, but finally it was done. Woody was officially permitted to take Flitarri's place. And so from being a mere spectator he now became one of the drivers in the race. It was a miraculous and complete change in his position and Woody didn't sleep much that night. There was too much to think about and too much to do.

17 ON THE following morning Flitarri was still adamant that he would not drive. The Italian, by no means a coward as his racing record showed, believed so strongly in the omen of birds that he would sacrifice his whole future rather than drive again in the race.

So it was Woody and Worm who took the Mark II to the starting line for the second and worst leg of the trip —the steep climb through Puebla to Mexico City. The service truck had arrived late in the afternoon and new brake linings and brake drums had been fitted on the four wheels.

Antonio took the news that Flitarri would not be driving any more with resignation. He spoke very little because he could say only a word or two in English. But he himself elected to stay with the pit crew. When he and Perez had finished servicing the car, they drove through the night to Mexico City to be there when the Mark II arrived. Perez was delighted that Woody was to drive.

So were Rocky and Mary Jane and Babs, though Woody knew that Mary Jane was worried. "You be sure to get to Mexico City in one piece, Woody Hartford," she said.

"Don't you worry, honey," said Woody. "This car and I are like twins. We just naturally work together."

Woody noticed that Worm was wearing a small silver chain around his neck. "What's that?" he asked.

"Christopher medal," said Worm, producing it. "Babs gave it to me." And he blushed.

Woody assumed that Worm would drive the next leg. He was older, more experienced, and had driven the car over this leg before in the survey. But Worm made Woody take the wheel.

"It's your car and your race from now on, laddie," he said. "I'm just coming along for the ride."

The Mark II had lost forty minutes on the lead Mercedes in the last leg. There were four legs to make this up in, two of them through mountains, two of them on the straight. The worst mountain leg lay ahead. It was no place for speeding. The wise thing to do was just hold position. But that forty minutes burned into Woody. If he could chop it down by fifteen minutes it would be very much to the good.

"If it's O.K. with you," said Woody, "I'm going to try to chew off a few of them in the mountains. We're badly behind. I don't feel like leaving it all till the last leg."

"Go ahead, laddie," said Worm. "This may be my last chance to die a single man." Woody didn't immediately get the significance of that remark.

The car was now part of a long queue drawn up before the starting line. One of the rules of the event was that the order of starting should be the same as the order of finishing in the previous leg. That meant that the

Mark II was no longer in the big sports-car group. It was back among the Lincolns, Cadillacs, Dodges, and Fords. The Mark II looked small and oddly out of place among the big sedans. But Woody was not worried about them. With superior cornering ability, he knew he could pass them all. The real competition lay ahead.

Finally the time came when the Mark II eased up to the starting line and awaited the green flag. The windshield had been replaced and a guard of iron bars put before it in case of further collision with birds. A steward checked off the name of the car. The starter held the green flag in one hand and a stop watch in the other. He raised the flag and brought it down in a bright arc. Woody let out the clutch and the Black Tiger roared away amid a storm of cheers.

For a quarter of a mile the road was straight, but uphill. Then it entered the mountains, and from that point on there was never more than half a mile of straight. Ahead was a Cadillac and beyond that a Lincoln. Woody tailed them for the first three miles, getting the feel of the car, becoming once again accustomed to its cornering characteristics and its acceleration with the new low-ratio rear-end gears. He found he had power to throw away on corners but with the low gears couldn't push her any faster than one hundred and forty-five on the short straights.

"Here goes," he shouted to Worm, and jammed the accelerator down. The Cadillac ahead had slowed for a bend. It was not one that was marked as dangerous on the map Woody had made and which Worm now had on his lap. Woody changed down to second nevertheless, passed the Cadillac, found the Lincoln ahead, swung wide, and passed on the inside. He felt good. The Mark II hadn't whimpered.

He slipped into high, flew over the top of a hill, found another Lincoln a quarter of a mile ahead entering a bend. He caught a glimpse of a bright blue tree trunk and heard Worm roar, "Switchback." Woody shut off and dropped into second. He wasn't sure whether there was just a more-than-right-angle corner ahead or something else as well.

There was something else. The road turned right in an acute angle, hooked around again to the left, dived down a short hill, and then snaked over a narrow bridge.

Woody was never certain where he passed the second Lincoln. He thought it was on the first bend. But pass it he did, spotted the bridge at the bottom of the hill, slipped into third, and stepped on the accelerator. He hit the bridge at one hundred and ten, screaming over it so fast that he felt like a rifle bullet aimed from one end of the bridge to the other. Then came a steep rise, and he was glad he'd changed down to third. The Mark II went up it like a bird, over the crown on a level stretch for two hundred yards, and then started climbing up the writhing road again.

Worm wrote something on a pad and put it on a clip board hanging from the dashboard. It read, "Good-by, Detroit." Woody grinned. He was through the Lincolns, Dodges, and Mercs. His own class lay somewhere ahead. He glanced upward for a second and saw through the ovoid glass of his goggles the road ahead, and caught his breath. The road was nothing less than a highway in the sky. It looped backward and forward above him, now disappearing, now reappearing, doubling upon itself over and over again, but mounting steadily all the while.

He caught sight of one car on it—a silver thing as small as a toy and he could not guess how many miles distant.

Then he turned his attention to the car again. He was in third and clocking one hundred and ten. Oil pressure showed eighty pounds, engine temperature a little above normal, gas tanks nearly full. It was nine-thirty. He had five more hours to go.

The going became really rugged now. The road was climbing steeply in a series of hairpins with about three hundred yards of straight between them. Even with safety belts the two were thrown against the side of the cockpit on each hairpin. Woody was conscious that his ribs were getting sore from this punishment. He changed down to second for each bend and then back to third and even to high for the straight. He began to worry about the clutch. It was taking a heavy beating, but the brakes were holding up. They'd better. There was a lot of mountain driving ahead.

On the fifth hairpin they caught sight of a Gordini just disappearing around the bend ahead of them. Worm shouted something which sounded like "Tally ho," and Woody jammed the accelerator down hard. Worm clipped another piece of paper to the board. It read "Mathews."

Mathews, Woody thought. That's the guy who tried

to get me disqualified. Wonder how he feels with me on his tail right now?

He glanced for a second over the side of the road. The road ran along the edge of a precipice and the drop was about seven hundred feet and the edge loose gravel. "Yes," he said to himself, "bet that guy Mathews is plenty worried now."

On the straight following the fifth hairpin Mathews' Gordini was in plain sight for about five seconds. Woody knew that Mathews must have seen the Black Tiger and must know who was driving it.

He caught Mathews on one of the hairpins and drifted round behind him in a fury of engine noise and screeching tires. He kept it that way for the next two hairpins. Mathews wasn't giving anything. He slowed down to forty for each hairpin and hugged the corner tight. Worm sat immobile in his seat and Woody wondered which of two courses to take. He could pass Mathews on the outside, with wheels only a few yards from the loose gravel leading to the precipice. Or he could wear the guy down until he lost his nerve and let Woody go by on the straight.

Woody decided to pass. He would have liked to wear Mathews' nerves raw. But it wasn't sporting. And he couldn't afford to waste the time. At the next hairpin he took it wide and clawed alongside the Gordini. He'd changed down to second. Then something happened. The Gordini edged closer and closer to the Mark II. It was drifting at full torque, and not quite under control. If it hit the Mark II, it'd go over the cliff.

For a split second Woody was frozen by panic. Then he changed up, hoping he had enough revs to pull ahead. The Mark II hesitated for a second between gears and then jerked forward.

Woody felt the warm blood flow back around his stomach as they pulled ahead of the Gordini. Worm leaned forward and clipped a piece of paper to the board. Woody glanced at it. It was a picture of a harp.

Woody was feeling really fine now. He felt good about passing Mathews and good that he hadn't frozen at the wrong moment. There had been times when he dreamed he'd frozen at the wrong moment on a bend and crashed. But in real life he hadn't. His confidence expanded enormously.

For the next hour he passed no cars. There was a Ferrari ahead. But the Ferrari was almost as good on corners as the Mark II. He contented himself with keeping it in sight and gradually gaining on it.

He glanced at the mileage indicator and the clock and figured his average speed. It was something more than seventy-eight miles an hour. That was really moving for this kind of driving. And brakes and clutch were still holding.

For most of the morning the sun had been shining brightly. Toward midday it clouded over. The air became colder and Woody guessed that they must be around eight thousand feet. A low overcast covered the sky and Woody, glancing swiftly to his left across a huge hidden valley in the mountains, saw that the peaks on the opposite side were hidden from view by clouds.

"Hope we don't get up among those clouds," he said to himself. "It'll be really hairy chasing around on this mountain in a white mist."

Half an hour later the mist closed in. There were just wisps of it at first, swatches of white which obliterated the road and mountains. Then there would be short intervals when it was clear.

But finally they came to a place where the mist was solid. They plunged around the corner into a huge mass of mist and visibility was reduced instantly to a few feet. Woody braked and shifted down to second and then to low. He turned on his headlights. The reflection from the mist nearly blinded him. He glanced at the speedometer. It seemed to him that they were going at a walking pace, but the speedometer read thirty miles an hour.

"What the heck am I supposed to do now?" said Woody to himself. He'd never driven a race in a fog before and wondered how many drivers had. He looked across at Worm for guidance.

"You got one of these medals?" asked Worm, producing his Christopher medal.

"Nope," shouted Woody.

"Well, maybe it'll work for the two of us," said Worm. "Keep her rolling."

Woody pressed the accelerator tentatively and the Mark II crept up to forty. Somewhere over the left side was the precipice. Woody couldn't see the side of the road so he didn't know where the precipice was. He could only just make out the cliffs on the right-hand side into which the road had been cut and he could see them for only thirty feet ahead. They were all he had to drive by and he made the best of it.

He had a lot of frights. A shoulder of cliff would loom out and he would swerve to the middle of the road, only to find that the road passed under the jutting shoulder and there was no need to swerve. He dropped back to thirty miles an hour. The other guys are running through the same stuff, he said to himself, so they can't be going any faster. Then it occurred to him that if he could make as much as five miles an hour faster than they he could make up a lot of time. And if he dared press to eight miles an hour faster, he would really be catching up.

It took all the resources of his will to speed up, but speed up he did. After a while thirty-five seemed normal. He pushed the speedometer up a fraction more. Then he caught sight of a tiny red light ahead. It was the taillight of the Ferrari. Should he pass? Could he pass? How wide was the road? Suppose he got alongside the Ferrari and found the road angled off sharp and he was headed over the edge of the precipice?

He waited, riding a few feet behind the Ferrari's rear bumper. Then the fog thinned a little. It wasn't much, but it was something. Woody hit the accelerator, pulled over, and steamed past the Ferrari. He chuckled when he got by. The road had been straight. The maneuver gave him confidence. He let the speedometer creep up to forty and held it there. They came on another car and passed that, too. And all the time they were climbing.

Suddenly the mist thinned and bright sunshine flooded down on the road. They were at ten thousand feet and had climbed up above the clouds which now lay below in a beautiful sea of down.

"We'll be able to make some time now," said Woody, and changed up to third. The air was cold and thin and cut the unprotected parts of his face with an edge like ice. Yet Woody was aware that he was sweating in his coveralls, and there was still three hours of this kind of driving ahead.

"What we need to come through alive," said Worm, "is radar."

18 THE LAST three hours of the second leg of the race, from Oaxaca to Mexico City, were every bit as grueling as the first three. The fog returned in patches and in places early rains had washed away part of the cliffs on the side of the road.

It was nothing to round a bend and find a boulder lying on the road ahead. The boulders had to be dealt with as they appeared. But the worst moment was the dash through Puebla where once again the police were not able to cope with the crowds.

The police were reinforced by members of the Mexican Army. These linked arms along the route through Puebla to keep the crowd back. But they could not withstand the pressure from the spectators. As the Mark II shot through an arch at the entrance to the city, with a Maserati ahead, the crowd burst through the military and police cordon.

Woody was horrified by the sight of a woman with a small child running across the road before him, between the Mark II and the Maserati. He shut off and hit the brakes. The Mark II slid sideways in a wild drift, for the slowdown was sudden. Woody fought the efforts of his rear wheels to catch up with his front wheels and send him spinning out of control with thousands of spectators on either side within a few feet of him. He caught a glimpse of the horrified face of the woman as the Mark II missed her by inches in a wild swerve. Then he saw the crowd leap forward toward him, flipped the steering wheel over, careened to the other side, hit the accelerator in second, and managed to regain control.

All the time the crowd was roaring with delight and excitement. It was a game for them, a game in which the loser died. Woody wondered if the host of fans in Puebla knew the terrible strain they were subjecting the drivers to with their wild game. After the ordeal of driving around the mountain road in a smother of fog, his nerves were tense as piano wires. The further ordeal of running the gamut of this crazy crowd at one hundred and thirty miles an hour was almost too much. Inches mattered in avoiding them, and if the car plunged into the spectators, a score would certainly be killed.

They were through Puebla in something under a minute. Woody found that he was gripping the steering wheel and that even the nerveless Worm was sitting bolt upright in the seat beside him. He deliberately relaxed and concentrated on the Maserati.

It took ten miles of driving to pass the big Maser. He crowded up to its tail on a corner and before the corner. Worm, who had been studying the map, put a piece of paper on the clipboard on which was written the single word "Go." That meant there must be a fair piece of straight ahead. Woody changed up to third and then to high and gave the Mark II the gas. He passed with ease and noted a bright orange rock ahead on the left. "Tight corner," he said to himself and blessed for the tenth time that morning Worm's "landscape painting." It was certainly proving its worth. He hit the brakes but though the pedal was firm, the car slowed reluctantly. He felt a surge of black fear. The brakes were fading. They'd go any minute. He stamped on the brake pedal again, slipped into neutral, revved up, and dropped into third. Somehow they made the corner.

Woody nudged Worm with his elbow and indicated the brake pedal. Worm nodded and pointed over the side. Woody understood. His tires were wearing thin. They were now within a hundred miles of Mexico City, something less than an hour's drive, for the road ahead was straighter though still over mountainous territory. The problem was, should he change tires? Or should he go on, hoping the rubber would hold up?

The Mark II carried two spare wheels. Wheel changing with her magnesium knockoff caps should take less than three minutes. On the other hand, he couldn't afford to lose three minutes. Nor could he afford a blowout. He weighed the question and discovered that his mental processes were slow. He was tired, far more tired than he had imagined, and he couldn't make a decision without an enormous effort.

Finally he decided that he ought to change wheels. He raised his left hand as a signal to any cars behind that he was going to slow down and pull off to the side. He put his foot on the brake. Nothing happened. The brakes had gone completely. How was he to stop? He could bring the Mark II to a standstill only by changing down to low and switching off the ignition. That might take another ten minutes. It would rob him of most of the lost time he had made up in the mountains. He indicated the brake pedal again, and Worm shrugged his shoulders. He understood. There was nothing to do but go on without brakes and with a blowout more probable with every mile.

For the rest of the way into Mexico City Woody concentrated on the race behind, not the one ahead. His job was to hold his position and prevent the Maserati behind from passing him. It was a grueling job, but he achieved it, using his gears mercilessly on corners. The road straightened for the last few miles into Mexico City itself. He couldn't afford to slow down here in a low gear.

This was the stretch on which all drivers would be going full bore. The problem was the crowd at the finish line. He'd probably cross it at one hundred and thirty-five, and the crowd would expect him to slow down. And he wouldn't be able to slow down—not for several miles.

Luck was with them when they reached Mexico City. The authorities, profiting from experience in previous races, had erected a huge enclosure of wire netting along the side of the road to keep the crowd back. And spectators in the city itself had been kept to the upper floor of houses so that the street to the finish line was clear of crowds.

Woody saw the checkered flag of the steward flash before him and changed down to third. He had finished at one hundred and thirty-eight miles per hour, side by side with a Jag which was slightly ahead of him. He slipped down to second, and then to first, and switched off the ignition. There was a loud report from behind and the whole rear of the car started to bump and wobble.

"Blowout," Woody shouted.

Suddenly he spotted a knot of people in the street, dead ahead. He was a long way past the finish line and the crowd thought there was no danger. He pulled the wheel over to the right to avoid the people. The Mark II leaned heavily to the left, made a gallant effort to remain upright, slammed broadside into a pile of hay bales, and came to a standstill.

"That's a heck of a way to stop an automobile," said Worm.

"If it hadn't been for those hay bales," said Woody, "the Mark II would be washed out right now. I don't think there's much damage done."

He undid his safety belt, climbed out of the seat, and experienced a sharp stab of pain in his left side. He winced, and Worm asked, "You hurt?"

"Nothing much," said Woody.

A little later a tow truck came and towed them to the garage area. Antonio and Perez were waiting and Woody told them of the crash stop. "Check the rear axle and suspension and brake lines," he said, and the two went to work immediately.

In the garage area there was a big scoreboard showing the elapsed time for each car from the start, and over the last leg.

"Mon," cried Worm, "we won this leg—eight minutes faster than the leading Mercedes. And on the two laps we're only twenty minutes behind with three more laps to go. We're still in the running and have a real good chance."

Woody nodded but he was very worried.

"Right now it's up to Antonio and Perez," he said. "They've got three hours to check for damage and change the rear-end gears. We're out of the mountains now and have got to change over to high screws. That's a two-hour job if everything goes without a hitch. If they run into trouble, we're out of the race."

Worm and Woody stayed with the two mechanics while they worked on the car. They were like a couple of surgeons operating on a dying patient with every second counting. Woody itched to get in and help them. But that would automatically disqualify the car. Only two mechanics could work on the cars for three hours, and an official stood by each car to see there was no extra help or extra time.

But at the end of the three hours Antonio and Perez had changed the rear-end gears, checked the rear-end suspension, and renewed the brakes. They were both dead beat but they'd done it. Woody began to realize more fully that the whole onus of the race was not on him alone, and that the honor of winning, if indeed he did win, was due as much to his two mechanics as to himself and Worm.

After their three-hour ordeal working on the Mark II, Antonio and Perez still could not rest. They had to drive on to Durango, the end of the next leg, to be there when the Mark II arrived.

"How are you feeling, Perez?" Woody asked.

"I have never been happier in my life," the Mexican replied. "Señor Worm, you think we work well?"

"Mon," said Worm, "you're as good a mechanic as I am, and I've not said that to anybody before."

Perez beamed, and Woody knew that he took the compliment not only for himself but for the Mexican people of whom he was immensely proud.

Before he dropped off to sleep that night, Woody thought of the Black Tiger team. There was a Scotsman, an American, a Mexican, and an Italian on it, and he smiled as he realized that in road racing there wasn't any such thing as nationality.

19 THE NEXT lap was in two parts. Over all it ran from Mexico City to Durango—a distance of five hundred and seventy-four miles. But it was to be made in two legs with a service stop of half an hour at León, two hundred and forty miles out of Mexico City.

The two mechanics, Antonio and Perez, would not be at León. They had gone on to Durango, and whatever servicing was done at León would have to be undertaken by Worm and Woody.

The road lay downhill for the first two hundred miles, snaking onto the great flat Mexican plateau.

Woody felt nervous and anxious at the start. He had not slept well during the night, his sleep disturbed by a variety of worries about the condition of the Black Tiger. He wondered whether some damage had been sustained in the crash stop which Perez and Antonio had not located. A little thing could cost them the lap and put them out of the running.

Mary Jane wished him luck and he was so nervous he almost snapped at her. She kept smiling, but he could sense that there were tears behind the smile and he felt wretched. He was thinking of this when the green flag fell and he released the clutch and shot over the starting line.

The new rear-end gears worked wonders for the Mark II's performance. The road was wide and had a good surface, permitting fast driving. Woody floored the accelerator and zoomed up on a Gordini ahead. He passed it on the straight without any trouble, and found a Ferrari ahead. He glanced at his speedometer and it read one hundred and sixty.

"Well, let's see what you can do, baby," he said, and pressed the accelerator pedal. The needle crept up to one hundred and sixty-five and then to a wavering one hundred and seventy-two. They were overhauling the Ferrari mercilessly.

In this section the road went through a series of gentle bends. It was not quite flat but undulated over a series of hills, so that visibility would sometimes be several miles and then be reduced to a few hundred yards by the intervention of a hill. The Mark II overhauled the Ferrari at the foot of one of these gentle slopes and rode neck and neck as the two flung over the crown of the hill. Suddenly Woody saw, perhaps a mile ahead, a black dot in the middle of the road.

What was it—a rock—a dog—a child?

Suddenly he realized it was a child who had wandered innocently into the middle of the road right in the path of the two cars racing toward it side by side. The child was utterly bewildered, standing stock-still while its mother beckoned from the side.

Suddenly the mother darted into the road after the youngster. Woody had only seconds to decide what to do. Instinct demanded that he slam on his brakes and change down. But a voice inside told him that that was what the driver of the Ferrari, neck and neck with him, was likely to do. They would remain side by side, occupying the whole road, and child and mother would be killed.

He steeled himself and hit the accelerator instead of braking, pulling over to the left away from the Ferrari. He saw the woman and her baby loom up and flash by, and felt the Mark II tremble and buck as her left side wheels went off the tarmac onto the dirt at the side of the road. For the next few seconds he fought for control of the car, plowing through the dirt at the side of the road. How he regained control he didn't know, but suddenly he was back on the tarmac and everything had returned to normal. Worm glanced behind and then pinned a scribbled note to the slipboard. It read: "O.K."

Woody relaxed. He was afraid that though he had missed the mother and her child, the Ferrari had not been able to. But he felt ten years older and for a few seconds suffered a fit of trembling and waves of nausea which were hard to fight off.

At León they did nothing but gas up, check oil, gearbox level, and change the two rear tires. Then they were off again down the road to Durango.

Driving at top speed, Woody found that the handling qualities of the Mark II changed considerably. Her steering became light, almost too light, and Woody was glad of the additional weight of the auxiliary gas tank up forward.

The high speed brought enormously increased hazards of its own. Slight depressions in the road were exaggerated into valleys. The car thundered to the bottom of them and then for an instant was subject to a weight of many tons before it took the opposing rise. Corners —even long, sweeping bends with plenty of room— were negotiated in seconds and Woody always felt a restriction in his stomach as he swept around them at full throttle, agonized at the thought that there might be someone in the road or a boulder which would wreck the car. He found he had to put such thoughts out of his mind firmly or he would give way to a tendency to back off on the throttle. And he couldn't afford to back off.

He hit one stretch of road, while negotiating a series of S-bends, which had been washed out and poorly repaired fifty miles out of León. The Mark II flipped in the air with all four wheels off the ground for a fraction of a second. It hit the ground with an impact of several tons and the rear of the car started to fishtail, waggling in jerks from side to side. Woody dared not touch his brakes. He backed off on the accelerator and then hit it again. The car pulled out of the fishtail and they went on.

They passed a Maserati which had pulled over to the side with some kind of trouble and found a Mercedes and Lancia ahead and gave chase. The driver of the Mercedes was running a rearguard race, more determined not to be passed than to pass anyone himself. Every time Woody sought for a loophole to pass he found it skillfully blocked. The man was undoubtedly one of the professional drivers of the Mercedes team acting under instructions, blocking for the lead Mercedes ahead. Woody boiled. He was losing time, his speed was down to one hundred and fifty, and still he couldn't get by.

They came to a long, sweeping curve to the left, going downhill. There was a concrete bridge over a dry gulch at the bottom of it, the ends of the bridge supported by huge balustrades of stone with sandbags before them.

The driver of the Mercedes hugged the inside of the corner, noted the bridge, and changed down. Woody had the same feeling in that moment as he had had the day he wrecked the original Black Tiger. It was a feeling of exhilaration and recklessness. Every instinct told him to change down, too, for the downhill bend was dangerous. He reached for the gearshift as he had done before and then took his hand off it.

He sensed Worm stiffening beside him, but he didn't change down. He knew the Mercedes wouldn't dare block on such a corner as this, that the driver must hug the inside. And he knew, too, that the Black Tiger had exceptional resistance to the huge centrifugal force developed in taking corners at high speed.

So he didn't change. Instead, he hit the accelerator and took the outside position. He saw the balustrades of the bridge leap toward him, saw the Mercedes on his left-hand side, and pushed the accelerator grimly to the floor.

The two cars entered the bridge neck and neck. They thundered across it side by side with the Mark II gaining. When they got to the other side Woody had an overlap. A minute more and he was ahead of the Mercedes with a Lancia roaring away before him.

The Lancia gave no trouble. It could corner like a cat but it didn't have the speed on the straight of the Black Tiger, Mark II. Woody passed and glanced at his speedometer. The needle was steady at one hundred and seventy-two. But the tach needle was resting against the pin at 8000 rpm. Woody backed off a little. No sense running the needle off the dial and maybe swallowing a valve. There were still two days of racing ahead. This wasn't the time to blow the works. Later he'd wring out of the Mark II every ounce of power it had.

Just before entering Durango, Woody passed Dave Kingston's D-Jaguar. It was no victory. The Jag was barely doing seventy and Woody learned later that it was missing on two of its six cylinders.

When he crossed the finish line at Durango and pulled into the official garage area, the scoreboard told him he'd won that particular leg, was now fifth in class, and only twelve minutes behind the lead car.

The whole city of Durango was wild about the Black Tiger. The car had come from way back in the pack to fifth place, won two legs, and was the dark-horse favorite to win.

Photographers and reporters swarmed around Woody and Worm and they were the center of a storm of flashlights for half an hour. Microphones were thrust in front of them and Woody didn't know what he said except that it was something about enjoying the race and hoping his luck would hold. The car was running perfectly and had given him no bad moments. He was surprised to learn that four cars in the big sports class had dropped out because of trouble of one kind or another on the last leg.

"What do you think of your prospects of winning?" was a question constantly put to him.

Woody's reply was always the same. "We'll have to see," he said.

He felt better at the end of the Durango lap than he had when they arrived in León. There he had had a return of the shakes on recalling how nearly he had come to killing the woman and her child. The only things that really bothered him now were his side and his hands. He had a big bruised area on his left side and whenever he pressed it he got a sharp pain. He suspected a broken rib from the collision with the hay bales in Mexico City. He'd have to have it x-rayed. But that would have to be later.

His hands gave him the most trouble. He'd driven all the way with gloves and when he peeled his gloves off he found his fingers were rubbed raw. There was a plum-colored area in the center of the palm of his right hand and he didn't know how it had got there. Then he figured that it was a bruise caused by working the gearshift. But he was not depressed any more, and that night held a council of war with Worm over the next leg—the second to last leg of the race from Durango to Chihuahua with a break at Parral.

This was the crucial leg, the one which would decide the issue of victory or defeat. It was the leg which must be won and it was, to all intents and purposes, a straight, flat run over an arrowlike route from Durango to Chihuahua.

Rocky, Mary Jane, Babs, Perez, and the silent Antonio were called into the council of war. It was one in which any contribution to achieve victory would be welcome although decisions would be up to Woody and Worm.

"As you know," said Woody when they were all together, "there're two more legs in this race—from here to Chihuahua, which is close to four hundred and fifty miles, and then the final spurt from Chihuahua to Juárez, which is only two hundred and twenty-five miles.

"We're twelve minutes behind the lead Mercedes and we've got to make most of that up tomorrow on the leg from here to Chihuahua. We can't rely on making up more than two or three minutes of lost time on the short last leg from Chihuahua to Juárez. So tomorrow's the day."

Nobody said anything.

"I've been doing some figuring," said Woody, "and I think we can reckon on the Mercedes averaging a hundred and thirty-five miles an hour over the leg to Chihuahua tomorrow. That means that if the lead Mercedes doesn't run into trouble, he'll reach Chihuahua in three hours and twenty minutes' elapsed time. There's a half-hour stop at Parral, as you know, but that doesn't count.

"If we are to win—and I want to emphasize that whether we have a chance or not will be decided tomorrow—we have to cover the distance in nine minutes less than the lead car, which, as I say, will probably be a Mercedes. That means we have to hit an average speed of a little more than a hundred and forty-two miles an hour.

"If we don't average a hundred and forty-two miles an hour for every minute of the leg tomorrow, we can't make it up on the last leg from Chihuahua to the finish line. The distance is too short. Now, has anybody got any suggestions?"

"You think the Mercedes is going to press that hard tomorrow?" asked Worm. "They've got a good lead. They may relax."

"We can't rely on them relaxing," replied Woody. "They're out not only to win but set a new record for this race."

"Señor Woody," said Perez, "I don't think the Mercedes team is going to be able to hold a hundred-and-thirty-five-miles-an-hour average."

"Why?" asked Woody.

"I just heard the weather report before I came here. It is for strong head winds all the way. That will cut down their top speed by fifteen, maybe twenty miles an hour."

"How reliable is this weather report?" asked Worm.

"I know the weather forecasting in this region," replied Perez. "When it concerns wind, it is always accurate. At this time of the year the desert heats up during the day when the sun is well up and cold air rushes in from the sea. There'll be bad winds and big dust storms tomorrow. I know. I would gamble my life on it."

"Would you gamble this race on it?" asked Worm.

"Yes," said Perez.

Worm turned to Woody. "If there are going to be heavy head winds tomorrow, the thing to do is to change back to the low-ratio rear-end gears. We won't get the driving power we need to buck head winds with those high-ratio gears we're using now."

Woody shook his head. "With the low screws she peaks out at somewhere around a hundred and fifty-five," he said. "We'd be handicapping the car terribly."

"No," said Worm, "we would not. We'd be helping her. Head winds are just like mountain climbing. There's an extra drag on the car, and you won't be able to wind her up to peak rpm in high unless you get those low screws. The kind of winds they're talking about will knock our top speed down to a hundred and forty with the high screws."

"Supposing it turns out to be calm?" said Woody. "The weatherman is often wrong. Supposing it was calm and we'd put in the low-ratio gears and could only make a hundred and fifty-five flat out?"

Worm shrugged. "You've got to think about it and then make a decision. It might be right or it might be wrong. You can't tell."

"Señor Woody," said Perez, "you can rely on the wind."

"How much service time we got on the car?" Woody asked.

"We have the full three hours," said Perez. "Nothing has been done yet."

Woody looked at Worm. "What do you say?" he asked.

"You're the driver," said Worm. "If I was driving I'd change the rear-end gears. I'd rack them down from 3.27 to 3.85. But I wouldn't let anybody know about it."

Woody nodded. "O.K.," he said to Perez, "change the gears and pray for a gale."

There was one other problem on his mind. That was whether he should let Worm drive this leg. His side was beginning to throb badly and his skinned fingers bothered him. He weighed the question in his mind and then made his decision. He'd done pretty well so far. It wouldn't be fair to turn the critical lap over to Worm. If they won, it would be swell for Worm. But if they lost, he would be the one to take the blame.

For the first time Woody realized that a racing driver takes the responsibility for losing as well as the credit for winning. That had never occurred to him before. He couldn't back out now that the pressure was on.

"Well," he said, "unless somebody else has got something to offer I guess that's it."

The conference broke up, and Worm and Woody went down to the garage area with Perez and Antonio. They stayed there until all the work on the car had been done, then they went to bed.

20

WOODY and Worm were up and breakfasted before dawn the following day. Woody had a hard time getting down a poached egg, a slice of toast, and a cup of coffee. Worm ate his way solemnly through a dish of ham and eggs with a side order of hot cakes. He seemed completely unperturbed, quite careless of all that hung on the issue of the race—first-prize money amounting to fifty thousand dollars if Mr. Tanner's twenty thousand were counted in, and national publicity for the Black Tiger, Mark II, which would result in many orders and establish it in the top rank of sports cars.

After breakfast the two went for a short walk in the predawn twilight. Woody doubted whether he could retain his breakfast and was sorry he'd eaten it. He was jumpy and irritable and every time he thought of the race, he felt a hot flush travel slowly down his spine. It settled always in his stomach and made him feel so weak that it seemed his legs could hardly carry him.

He was grateful that Worm said nothing. His side ached abominably and he was glad that it was cold, for the cold quieted the smart of his fingers, stripped of skin. When they entered the garage area shortly after five, Woody said, "I feel like I'm going to die."

"You'll live," said Worm.

"Did you used to feel like this when you raced in Europe?" asked Woody.

"Sure," said Worm. "I remember eating three breakfasts before the Tourish Trophy in Ireland in 1935 and I couldn't keep one of them down. They cost me ten shillings and sixpence halfpenny."

Although he was feeling so wretched, Woody laughed. Money was always a great point with Worm.

Kurt Kreuger came over to see them for a minute. "Good luck," said Kurt, and offered his hand.

"Thanks," said Woody, "same to you."

Kurt in his Mercedes was positioned just ahead of the Mark II. Ahead of him were a Ferrari, a Lancia, and then the two factory Mercedes in the lead.

The cars moved out of the garage area and took their places before the starting line. It was five-thirty and the start was to be at six.

"I don't feel any wind," said Woody. "Cripes, I wish we hadn't changed those gears."

"The wind will come up later," said Worm. "Forget about all that. All you got to do now is drive as best you can with what you've got."

What Woody said was true. There was no wind. The air was so still that it seemed the whole world was watching and waiting for the start.

Worm patted Woody on the thigh. "All a man can do is his best," he said. "Relax. Winning doesn't make a great driver. It's trying to win that counts."

Six o'clock came at last. There was the usual huge crowd. The noise from them suddenly stilled. All eyes focused on the starter standing ahead and to the side of the lead Mercedes. Suddenly he jumped into the air and brought the flag down. The Mercedes roared off and its engine noise was drowned in the shout of the crowd. Then there was silence. The second Mercedes went away. Then the Lancia. Eight minutes past six and it was the Mark II's turn.

Woody's legs were visibly trembling and he was ashamed that Worm would see. But he had forgotten the pain in his side and was watching the starter. The flag fell, he released the clutch, and shot away, followed by a wave of shouts and a vast fluttering of hats and hands from the spectators. He heard them shouting *"Olé, el Tigre Negro,"* which had become a kind of battle cry during the race and he knew that the people were cheering not only for the car but for the Mexican mechanic who was one of the pit crew. He suddenly felt very warm toward them.

In a matter of a few seconds after the start the Mark II was in high with the accelerator floored. The tachometer showed eight thousand rpms and the speedometer one hundred and fifty-five miles per hour. Kurt's Mercedes was a good three miles ahead, visible as a small dot on the broad, straight road and drawing away. He must be clocking one hundred and sixty at least, Woody thought, and the Lancia would by now be at least thirty miles away.

Woody backed off on the accelerator and watched the rpms drop on the tach. He glanced at the speedometer and the needle was still shivering around one hundred and fifty-five. It was foolish to use maximum rpms when they added nothing to his road speed. And because of the low rear gears he was trapped with a top speed of one hundred and fifty-five. And there was still no wind.

"Well," he said to himself, "we gambled and lost. We reckoned on a wind and there isn't any wind. We're outclassed by fifteen maybe twenty miles an hour."

It was worse than that. A Gordini steamed past them as if they were standing still to be followed by a Ferrari. Woody glanced at Worm, his agony showing on his face. Worm shrugged. Then he took his pad and wrote something on it and pinned it to the clipboard. It read: "Half an hour will tell." He'd been working with a slide rule computing speeds. If the wind didn't come up heavy in the next half-hour and from dead ahead, they could never make up the time lost.

Another car passed—a Ferrari. The driver gave Woody a puzzled look. Then Worm jabbed with his forefinger, indicating the horizon ahead. A few minutes before it had been a clean, light line against the blue sky. Now the horizon was blurred. It could be seen only in patches. The rest was obscured by a light brown fog. Worm clipped another sheet to the clipboard. It read, "WIND. Tally ho."

The wind struck them like a wall. The whimper and roar created by their own hundred and forty-five miles an hour through the still air now increased to deep rumbles and high shrieks. The Mark II was slowed momentarily, as if she had run into a huge barricade of foam rubber. Woody stamped on the accelerator. The speedometer had dropped back with the wind to one hundred and twenty. He coaxed it up to one hundred and forty, then one hundred and forty-five. It was not a steady pace. Sometimes the speed dropped as the velocity of the wind momentarily increased. Then it picked up again. But the speedometer never showed less than one hundred and thirty-five.

With the wind came dust—terribly fine cutting dust off the face of the desert, clouds of it whirling in spirals over the road. Soon the windshield was caked with a patina of light brown silt. At times the road would be momentarily obscured. But Woody didn't let up. He nerved himself to keep the accelerator on the floor. He kept going at top speed and blessed Worm's foresight which had resulted in the installation of the low gears.

One thing he was certain of. None of the cars ahead had changed their rear-end gear ratios, otherwise they could not have passed him. He had, he was sure, at least six miles an hour on them.

Thirty-five minutes from the start Woody swept by the Ferrari that had passed him earlier. Twenty minutes later he had regained his former position. The wind favored him in every way. It would prolong the over-all time for this leg. It would give him a margin of speed for a greater length of time over the lead cars. It would insure victory—if . . .

There were a lot of ifs—if the wind held to the finish line at Chihuahua. If the wind didn't change directions. If the silt streaming into them at a cumulative speed of something like two hundred miles an hour didn't get driven into the fuel system or pump to clog the fuel-injection jets. If his tires held out under the additional abrasion of the fine silt which now covered the road.

Fifty miles outside of Parral they found Kurt Kreuger in his Mercedes. They bore down inexorably upon him. They were about to pass when the Mark II started missing and Kurt pulled away.

"Dust," said Woody to himself, "in the fuel-injection jets." He kicked out the clutch, stamped on the accelerator, and let the clutch back in. The engine coughed, shook, and then roared to life. They came up on Kurt again, crept alongside him, saw him wave, and went ahead. Somewhere up in front now there were only four cars—the Lancia, a Ferrari, and the two Mercedes leading.

They found the Ferrari halfway between Parral and Chihuahua. The stream of dust from it made it look more like a rocket than a car. The wind had increased so that it was all Woody could do to hold the Mark II at one hundred and thirty-five. The Ferrari kept appearing and disappearing in the dust clouds. They crept down on it until there was but a quarter of a mile between the two cars. Suddenly the Ferrari seemed to collapse. It went over on one side and spun in a long, slow curve down the road. Woody didn't see what happened to it. He zipped by and heard an explosion, but he guessed the trouble. The Ferrari had blown a tire and spun out.

Three times before they got to Chihuahua the engine missed for a few seconds and then picked up again. Woody tried to figure out where the trouble was. Was it in the fuel-injection system? Was it in one of the filters in the gas line? Was it the plugs? Was it a short in the distributor system? Or was it in the fuel pump?

He decided the most likely place was the fuel pump. They'd been using the same high-speed pump, renewing the points at the end of each lap all the way from the start. They'd never switched on the fuel pump from the auxiliary tank because they'd never run low on gas. But had it been serviced or checked?

Woody reached forward to a switch on the dashboard and cut in the auxiliary tank and its pump. The switch over was made without a single miss. Woody blessed Perez and Antonio. They hadn't let him down on a detail that in the press of other matters they might have overlooked.

The wind continued all that day until late in the afternoon. When the Black Tiger crossed the finish line at Chihuahua to complete a race which had been run in the teeth of a gale, Woody had made up nine and a half minutes and was now only two and a half minutes behind the lead Mercedes.

He had done it only because of the change in the rear-end gears—a change advocated by both Worm and Perez. The critical leg had been won by the mechanics more than by the driver. As he suspected, none of the other cars had changed their gears and so their top speeds had been below that of the Mark II.

There remained now the final dash to Juárez on the United States border. It was a short run of but two hundred and twenty-five miles. The weather report was once more for heavy winds and again a conference was held as to what should be done.

Woody was for retaining the low-ratio gears. But Worm opposed him. "The wind won't come up before ten o'clock," he said. "That's what it did today. With the start at six, the race will be over before the gale starts. We should change back to the high gears."

"That is true," said Perez, who would have to do the work. "The leg tomorrow is high speed to the finish line. You have nothing to do but put your foot on the accelerator and keep going. You will need the high gears." It was agreed to install them.

"We've got two and a half minutes to make up," said Woody. "And we've only got two hundred and twenty-five high-speed miles to do it in. There are three cars ahead—the two Mercedes and the Lancia. They'll start each of them a minute ahead of us. That means we have to pass the Lancia and one of the Mercedes. And what worries me is that the two Mercedes are driving as a team—the one behind blocking for his teammate. It's going to be tough."

Worm shrugged. "It won't be any tougher than any of the races you've driven before," he said. "It'll be easier. There're no corners to worry about. Just get going and keep going and that's all there is to it."

The following morning Woody all but decided to turn the Mark II over to Worm to drive. His hands were so raw he felt they were on fire. His side was one mass of pain. He hadn't slept well and his eyes felt as though they were full of gravel. But he didn't ask Worm to drive for the same reason as before—that if they lost then Worm would take all the blame.

Again in the minutes immediately preceding the start of this final leg he had waves of nausea and his head reeled. He was far more tired than he had realized and although it would all be over in the next two hours, he didn't know how he was going to get through them.

The two Mercedes roared off down the road, then the Lancia, and then the flag fell for the Mark II. Woody released the clutch, felt a stab of pain through his torso as the car flung forward, and changed up into high.

Two hundred and twenty-five miles, he said to himself. Two and a half minutes to be made up. He tried to wrestle with the figures but his brain would not respond. He had worked them out the evening before, but he could not recall them now. The thing to do was to catch and pass the Lancia and one of the Mercedes. That was all.

Woody could see the Lancia ahead, a toy car on the straight, flat road, with ahead of it another dot, which would be the rear Mercedes. He pressed the accelerator down and watched the speedometer creep to one hundred and sixty, then one hundred and sixty-five, and then one hundred and seventy. The road streaked beneath the wheels at nearly three miles a minute. His hands were burning, hurting so badly that the pain extended into his wrists and forearms. His arms seemed heavy.

After fifteen minutes the Lancia seemed no nearer. It had retained its position although they had both gained on the Mercedes. How much had they gained? A hundred yards and fifteen minutes had gone. A hundred yards in fifteen minutes meant less than a quarter of a mile in an hour. It wouldn't do.

Woody pushed the accelerator pedal to the floor. The speedometer needle crept to one hundred and seventy-five. The Lancia drew a little closer. It grew bigger, and Woody figured that he had perhaps three or four miles an hour on it. But it was a very tentative three or four miles an hour. Every little detail of body design counted now. The air flow over the car was all important.

Gradually he drew up on the Lancia and established an overlap. His front wheels were abreast of the Lancia's rear wheels. The two cars hurtled along the road at nearly three miles a minute, side by side. Neither driver looked at the other. Woody knew that if anything happened now—if there was a blowout or if he hit a bump in the road, the two cars would be thrown together and he would be killed.

The Mercedes was dead ahead, not more than two lengths away. And only a hundred yards farther on was the other Mercedes. The four cars formed a pack streaking over the highway, fighting for inches.

They came to a long, slow curve in the road. It was not a corner—just a gentle bend to the right through an angle of less than fifteen degrees. But it favored the Lancia, which also had the advantage that the Mercedes in front was breaking the wind for it. The Mark II slipped back so that Woody no longer had an overlap.

In the next mile Woody fought back alongside the Lancia once more. He crawled inexorably alongside, got neck and neck, and finally slightly ahead. Then the Mercedes glided gracefully across the road in front of him. Woody never knew whether the driver did this purposely, but the maneuver favored him. The Mercedes had been breaking the wind for the Lancia. Now it was breaking the wind for the Mark II, and it picked up speed immediately. Woody decided to take the Mercedes on the right-hand side. He inched up behind it and then pulled over to the right.

"Baby," he said, "give me everything you have—and just a little more."

He had the accelerator pedal pressed down as far as it would go. The Mark II pulled alongside the Mercedes, gaining gradually, the wind roaring over the windshield and drowning out the note of the engine.

"A little more, baby," said Woody. "Just a little more."

Gradually he pulled ahead. It was a matter of inching forward then dropping back and then gaining again. But he made it. The speedometer needle hovered at a miraculous hundred and eighty-two miles per hour.

Worm, crouching low in his seat, stabbed with a finger up ahead. Woody thought he was pointing to the lead car, the other Mercedes. But he looked past it for a second and saw a dark spot on the flat and distant horizon.

Juárez, he thought. The finish line. If he could hold his position for the next five minutes, he had won.

He permitted himself a glance in the rear-view mirror. The Lancia and Mercedes were battling it out no more than ten yards to the rear. Five minutes to go, he said to himself, and repeated it. He had forgotten about his hands now and the pain in his side. He felt a tremendous surge of confidence and elation. He looked across at Worm and saw Worm's mouth was working so he shouted something. But Woody could not hear what it was above the high roaring of the wind. Then he guessed what Worm was doing. Worm was singing—singing some kind of Highland Scots war song which the wind whipped back to scatter in the dust of the Mexican desert.

The dark mark ahead had grown denser and could now be distinguished as a host of people lining the road behind a barrier of wire netting. A banner stretched across the road overhead, flashed by, and a man brought down a checkered flag.

The Mexican Road Race was over. And the Black Tiger had won!

21

IT WAS two weeks later and Woody and Worm were back in Hermosa Beach.

The Black Tiger, Mark II, had won the Mexican Road Race by the slim margin of three seconds. There was only a difference of twelve seconds between the first four cars. The finish had been that close.

Many things had happened and at a hectic pace right after the race. There had been a big banquet in Juárez at which the announcement of the Black Tiger's victory was officially made. Worm and Woody had received a total of forty-three thousand dollars in prize money from Mexican sources. They had also won the twenty thousand dollars offered by the eccentric Mr. Tanner. This, of course, had been turned over to Rocky and Babs, for it belonged to the company. But company headquarters in Italy were so elated at the result that they gave it back to Rocky, who was using it to expand the Black Tiger Sales Agency.

Already the Black Tiger, Mark II, was the most famous sports car in America. The car had established itself in the most grueling race in the world. It was receiving, through Mr. Tanner's advertising campaign, saturation publicity, and the demand was at a peak and likely to stay there.

Of the forty-three thousand dollars' prize money which Worm and Woody had received they had given half to Perez and Antonio. Antonio returned to Italy, and Perez was certainly the happiest citizen of the Republic of Mexico.

Woody then had some ten thousand dollars with which to start married life with Mary Jane. Nor was he the only one setting down the road of matrimony. Worm, right after the victory banquet, had proposed to Babs and been accepted.

"A very sensible woman," he told Woody. "She'll make an uncommonly good housekeeper, being thrifty with her money."

Woody was reviewing all this alone with Mary Jane in the living room of her house. His side was strapped once again to rest a rib, which x-rays had revealed was fractured, but the future was as bright as it could possibly be.

"I'll never get over being proud of you for winning," said Mary Jane, who had now completely changed her views on road racing and would not hear of Woody following any other career.

"Winning?" said Woody slowly. "You know why Worm and I won? Because we had a swell car and were lucky enough to have the chance to drive it. Because we had a pit crew that worked like they were trying to save their own lives all through the race, and got less sleep than Worm and I did. Because we were lucky and didn't have a blowout or any bad trouble all the way.

"And because there were a lot of other pit crews, and a lot of other swell cars, and a lot of other drivers, maybe better than us, who did their darnedest—and lost.

"That's why we won."

Mary Jane nodded. She knew that what Woody was saying was true. And she loved him for saying it.

247   F.W.